Craft

Meet-A-Pet

Gideon's Way

Your Verses

Cover by Susan Mayer.
ISBN 0-85116-646-6

A Dish called Happiness

Take an attractive daughter and a father
who likes playing Cupid. Add a shy but eligible
young man and stir well . . .

D
AD, where are you? Something's burning!" Susan had
dumped her District Nurse's bag on the nearest chair and
hurried through to the kitchen. Her father was already there,
contemplating something jet black and smoking like Vesuvius on the
kitchen table.

"What is it — was it?" She laughed, knocking her cap squint.

"It was, and still is," her father informed her meticulously, "a
Victoria sponge."

"But . . . who made it?"

"It was I," he said grandly.

"You?" She couldn't keep the amazement out of her voice.

"Your cap is crooked, Susan. Have you had a bad day?"

"No, not until now." She removed her hat. "But you don't know
how to bake."

"One is never too old to learn," her father replied.

"I've never in my life known you to heat up so much as a tin of
baked beans," she laughed. "For as long as I can remember, you've
regarded cookers with the superstition of primitive man confronted by
fire for the first time, and you know it as well as I do."

"Now, let's not exaggerate," Mr Rickard said mildly.

"Actually, I've just made a pot of tea. Care to join me?"

"Oh, tea. Well, that's something we couldn't live without," Susan
said, as she eased off her shoes and coughed again. "Do you think you
could carry your burnt offering outside before we choke to death?"

"I suppose I shall have to honour the birds with my first culinary
effort," he agreed, picking it up.

"If they come knocking on the door tomorrow with bent beaks and
charcoal poisoning, refer them to the local hospital, and not to me,"
she called after him. "My schedule's full to overflowing."

Complete Story
by DOROTHY L. GARRARD

"Indigestion tablets?" Hugh Godwin queried, putting the bottle on
the counter. "This isn't the usual sort of thing you carry, Susan."

"They're for my father, I have the feeling he'll be needing them
soon. He's just taken up baking," she explained, slipping the bottle
into her shoulder-bag.

"Could you fill these two prescriptions for me, Hugh? I'll call back
around twelve. Can't stay today, I'm run off my feet."

He watched her as she left the shop. Her thick fair hair was coiled
neatly into the nape of her neck and her calm, capable manner inspired
the utmost confidence in her patients.

And though she had his complete admiration, that total self-
possession had always daunted him.

But if Susan's confidence rather unnerved Hugh, it didn't have the
same effect on her father.

A DISH CALLED HAPPINESS

"Dad," Susan said tentatively, just over a week later, "how long is it going to take for this fad to wear off?"

"Fad?"

"You can't really be interested in turning out one Victoria sponge after another?" she said, a little exasperation in her voice.

He regarded his fourth sponge thoughtfully.

"I just need practice, that's all, and I am improving . . . I know this one has a hole in the middle like the village duck pond, but at least it isn't soggy, or pretending to be a biscuit."

"But, Dad, why? We never did eat much cake, and you seemed perfectly content with stuff from the baker's for Saturday tea."

"I've only done what you've been suggesting I should do ever since I retired. I've taken up a hobby."

"Baking? A hobby?"

"My old mate Charlie Bowen bakes pottery in an oven and has a stall at the fête, and everyone says clever old Charlie, even though some of those Toby jugs of his are enough to frighten the gargoyles off the parish church. So why shouldn't I bake things in ovens, too?"

"You wouldn't care to take up cordon bleu cookery?" Susan suggested hopefully.

"I appreciate your cunning," he laughed. "But it's not the same. That kind of food is just fuel for the engine but this is artistic. Look at the colour plates in your cookery book."

"Cakes rarely turn out like their pictures," Susan laughed.

"If somebody else can do it, why can't I?" he persisted.

★   ★   ★   ★

"How's your father's indigestion?" Hugh enquired when she appeared again.

"Getting better, along with his cakes!" She smiled. "I must say, he's become quite professional and decided he's found his true vocation," Susan smiled.

"Many of the best chefs are men," Hugh remarked.

"A nice cordon bleu dinner I wouldn't mind, now and then." She sighed. "Still, I've never seen him so totally involved in a hobby before."

"What started him off?" Hugh asked curiously.

"He said he was in the kitchen making tea," Susan explained, "when quite suddenly he fancied a piece of home-made sponge, which Mother used to make quite regularly. He just took it into his head to try — and that was it. He was hooked."

"I wish he'd papered a wall on such a whim." She sighed. "Or pulled a weed or two. Heaven knows, I need a gardener or decorator more than I need an obsessional cook!"

All was quiet on the home front when Susan returned. She poked her head round the kitchen door.

"Oh, dear," she said. "Another disaster, Dad?"

6

"Look a little closer," he said, proudly. "It may be black, but behold — no smoke, no fire! Guess what?"

She gazed at the dark confection, impressed. Smooth and beautifully risen with a resilient looking surface, it was flanked by basins full of beaten concoctions, and her father was tearing open a packet of chocolate dots.

"The smell is enough to put an inch on my waist," Susan said. "What is it?"

"Devil's food cake. It has to be left for the frosting to set," he said regretfully. "In the meantime I knocked off a little sponge to be going on with, with a new kind of filling."

THE next time she went into the chemist's, Hugh leaned conspiratorially over the counter. "I think I see a ray of hope for you, Susan. Your father went up the High Street half an hour ago, striding out like a two-year-old. Could he have taken up jogging instead?"

"I'm sorry to disappoint you," Susan explained. "He was merely on his way to the library. He's on the trail of cookery books, having worked his way through all of mine and Mother's old scrapbook. He wants to try something more demanding now."

"You're beginning to sound quite annoyed," Hugh said, surprised.

"Well, it's so unnerving," Susan said, fidgeting with her belt buckle. "I can't open a single cupboard without finding a cake inside. I've given several away — with a few slices missing of course, since Dad tastes them immediately. But people wonder what's wrong with them, and it's such an odd situation to explain.

"Dad tried giving some away too, down at the social centre." She grinned. "He got a bit of criticism about the ones that weren't so good, and worse, certain ladies got the idea he was demonstrating what a useful husband he would make!"

★   ★   ★   ★

It had become force of habit to go straight through to the kitchen, but this time Susan backed out again to sneeze.

"What on earth are you making now?" she asked.

"Apple strudel." The reply was cut short by a sneeze.

"I suppose this lot is the cloud over the Alps?" Susan beat at the haze of flour in the air. "Do you have to throw the pastry at the table like that?"

"I'm kneading it," her father said, with a superior air. "All good pastry cooks lift the mixture into the air and hurl it on to a floured slab from a good height — at least so the book says.

"Imagine — it has to be stretched so thin that you can read a newspaper through it." He wiped his brow.

Continued on page 10.

YOUR VERSES

A SPECIAL PEN FRIEND

We haven't met, we're miles apart,
But you live here, in my heart.
Your letters come, you're in my room,
Your words dispelling any gloom.

I spend time with you on a page,
We share our joys, our fears, our rage.
You understand. You care so much,
And through our letters two lives touch.

You pick me up when I am low
And you rejoice when I'm aglow,
I hope my letters do the same —
To keep you happy is my aim.

Your photo looks at me and smiles,
Your love emits across the miles.
This flow of words will never end
For you are, indeed, my special friend.

Mrs E.H., Gwynedd.

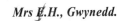

LAST CHANCE

We've only got a little time together
Yet we use the days for hurting — then we cry.
Our love's not growing stronger
While the making-up takes longer
And deep down I feel we're saying our goodbyes.

It's a pity that we can't agree to differ
For it doesn't do to always share one view.
Think how hectic life would be
If you always followed me,
And how dismal if I always copied you.

We never know when we may lose each other
And there'll come a day when we will surely see
All the lonely hours that grow
Into lonelier days will show
There'll be no happy thoughts for company.

So let's try a little harder in the future
Just a bit of give and take is all that's due,
For I know you really care
And I want the world to share,
In the knowledge that I really do love you.

P.S. Enfield.

Meet A Pet

Here's a special selection of your favourite pet pictures.

Jake

Mrs Sue Taylor's pet Standard poodle, Jake, just loves getting into mischief.

Mrs Carol Wolstencroft's neighbour's cat likes to make herself at home!

⇩

Sherry and Sophie take their ease. The two dachshunds are the much-loved pets of Mrs Joan Machan of Upton.

Sherry & Sophie

Bobby

Bobby is all dressed up with somewhere to go! Bobby is the much-loved pet of Mrs Dorothy Hutchinson of Southbourne.

Heidi

Sinbad says he's not for recycling! This delightful pic of Chrissie Nee's cat was sent in by Mrs Holdom of Burnham-on-Sea.

Sinbad

Heidi adjusts her picture to its best advantage! Her owner, Miss Joyce Duckworth, says Heidi often admires her photograph!

9

A DISH CALLED HAPPINESS

Continued from page 7.

"I'd go and have a cup of tea, if I were you — your uniform's getting a paler shade of blue by the minute."

"How can I?" Susan moaned. "I can't even see the kettle across the room! And if you want any dinner, Dad, you'd better get a move on. You've had the kitchen while I've been out all day, and I'm hungry even if you're not."

"Have a piece of . . ." He noticed her expression. "Yes, I'm sorry, it's taking longer than I expected. I only have to put the filling in and shape it into a horseshoe. Tell you what, fetch us some fish and chips — my treat. We can have this for pudding."

When he carried it from the oven there was a two-minute silence, before Susan said faintly, "Couldn't you at least cut down on the size of your concoctions?"

He stared at the solid mass of apple strudel, bubbling aromatically at the seams.

"Yes, it was one of those take a dozen-eggs-type recipes, but the trouble is, I get confused if I mess about with quantities."

There wasn't a lot to say to that, Susan thought.

She took Hugh a piece of strudel and left a chunk in the cottage hospital kitchen, but it took almost a week to get rid of it. Meanwhile, her father produced a mocha nut gateau and threw together a batch of rock cakes just to fill up the oven.

"Dad — I don't want to be a wet blanket, but it really is a problem. Even the birds have gone on strike. They're getting too fat for take-off."

"Couldn't you take some cakes with you on your rounds?" her father enquired.

"Become a cake salesman?" Susan said. "You've got to be joking!"

"Couldn't your boyfriend take some?" her father reflected.

"My . . . my who?" Susan spluttered.

"You know — young Hugh Godwin, really nice fellow. I can't understand why it's taking so long for things to develop there, you've known him long enough. If you had a brood of children, Susan, there would be no problems about getting rid of my cakes."

For a second she was speechless.

"Young Hugh," Susan said scarlet-faced, "is in his late thirties, like me, and chooses his own girlfriends. In fact he was engaged once."

"What's that got to do with it? It was years ago and you two have had your noses together over his counter for years."

"We're just good friends, in the best possible meaning of the words," Susan declared.

"By far the best basis for marriage," her father agreed blandly. "Your mother was my best friend, and I hers."

"Dear old Dad," Susan deliberately kept her voice light though her lingering blush spoiled the effect. "Has it never even occurred to you that it takes two? I've always been plain and I'm not getting any younger."

"Plain! Goodness!" Her father was astonished. "How could you say such a thing when you're the image of your mother!"

"I've also got your stubborn single-mindedness and forth-right tongue! Mother was so sweet and gentle that no-one ever noticed she wasn't beautiful."

"She was beautiful to me!" he argued, quite perturbed.

"What I need, then, is a man who sees me with eyes like you," Susan soothed him gently. "Meanwhile, don't think you've diverted me from the question of those cakes. The last thing Hugh would want — even if he did fall for my particular brand of antiseptic — is a cake dispensary."

Though she had dismissed Hugh as a diversion, her father's unexpected perception had flustered her a little. She had always been fond of Hugh, but knew that in his eyes romance and the practical Susan didn't go together, so she'd long resigned herself to being "just a good friend".

Now she wondered if other people saw her association with Hugh the way her father did, pitying her while she waited in vain for something to develop. She wished heartily he had kept his observations to himself.

SUSAN left her father staring into space over his breakfast cup next morning, but thought less in the coming week about the cake problem than about Hugh Godwin.

Perhaps it would be better to pop into the chemist's less often in case people were gossiping about it, she decided. She couldn't bear the thought of embarrassing him.

She missed their friendly encounters however, and still found herself thinking about Hugh. So it wasn't until she'd soaked away the rigours of a particularly hot and busy day in a cool, scented bath that she realised there was no evidence of the day's baking session, apart from a piece of lemon cake with her evening coffee.

"This tastes very nice indeed." Susan complimented him. "What happened to the rest?"

"I thought seriously, and came up with an answer to the problem."

"You're wearing a very complacent smile," she quizzed. "Oh, by the way, I've just noticed extra garden chairs outside. Been having a party?"

"Ask no questions and worry no more. Dear old Dad has everything under control. You're looking very tired lately, my dear. Isn't it about time you took a few days off?"

"As a matter of fact, I could get away this weekend, if it's all right with you," Susan said, thoughtfully. "There are no births imminent, nor any other foreseeable crises on the horizon. I'll ask for someone to do my routine calls." She began to feel quite excited.

"I'll ring Jenny, she's been wanting me to visit for ages. At least I can leave you this time in the safe knowledge you won't starve," she added.

Returning on Sunday evening, Susan paused, aghast, at the garden gate. The front lawn was strewn with garden chairs, stools, a couple of wicker bedroom chairs and several from the kitchen.

Continued on page 14.

Miniature Marvels

The tiny harvest mice climbing the stalks of ripe wheat make an enchanting sight, and remind Gideon of an act of kindness to a certain spellbound young lad . . .

WHENEVER possible, we try to grow a small grain crop on Croft Douglas to help feed our flock of birds and animals, knowing that any leftovers will be appreciated by the "wild ones".

The best laid land lies along the lochside, so that's where we plant, in soil surrounded by hazel trees. It's a natural suntrap all summer and, although not planted until late in May, the grain soon grows and ripens.

Watching the field when a light west wind blows, it almost looks like a little loch rippling with waters of gold, while scarlet poppy blooms bob up and down between the wavelets, to paint the pattern of a perfect daytime dream.

But some of the grain is blowing the other way, against the wind, thanks to a pair of harvest mice making their way to the top, curling their tails around the stalks to give them a firm grip.

The harvest mouse must surely be one of the smallest mammals we have here in the Highlands, just a tiny two inches of burnished golden brown with little white tummies and round heads that are mounted by even smaller elfin-like ears, making their bright black

eyes huge in comparison.

The harvest mice remind me so much of my schoolboy days when I longed for a pet of my own.

One Saturday morning my mother, who was the soul of understanding, pressed a shilling into my hand, saying in a matter-of-fact way, "There's a show and sale of pets at Picardy Place today. Go and get yourself one."

At the time we stayed at Fairmilehead, in a house my father had built at the foot of the Pentland Hills. It was quite a long way from central Edinburgh and the tyres of my small bicycle were almost smoking when I finally reached the pet show in Picardy Place.

THE big doorman looked down at me doubtfully, then he raised his bushy eyebrows, permitting me to pass through the large swing doors to Paradise — rows and rows of rabbits, fluffy white angoras brushed until they looked like powder puffs, black silky-furred chinchillas, and many other exotic breeds.

But it was the sophisticated show mice that particularly fascinated me. I paused at a little glass-fronted cage with a

red card clipped on top which said, "Cinnamon Mice. First Prize".

They were such a beautiful pair with subtle shades of chocolate and cream. The cinnamon was

12

Illustration by
Michelle Ross.

traced on their cream tummies which the tiny mice showed off as they stretched up the glass and beckoned with a "come closer" signal from their tiny forepaws, while eager black eyes and silver-tipped, twitching whiskers seemed to send out pleading messages like, "please be my friend."

I had the feeling I was being watched and turned around to find a man with a face like a full moon beaming down at me and saying, "Would you like them?"

I could only nod my head and produce the silver shilling. The kindly, moon-faced man patted my shoulder.

"It's a present," he said. "I saw the way you looked at them, and I know they'll be safe with you."

I called my cinnamon mice Rinty and Tintin after a shepherd dog I had seen in a film. I took Rinty to school in my blazer pocket and he learned to stay there until I whistled, then he would pop out to career about and so became a great favourite with the other boys.

Meantime, Tintin produced a family of seven and my school chums produced their pocket money, but I remembered the kindly, moon-faced man and only gave a little mouse to someone I knew he would be safe with.

WATCHING all the **harvest mice had given me a good idea just what to get my daughter, Shona, for her birthday. As soon as possible I paid a visit to the pet shop in Perth and, after a great deal of thought, purchased a little black and white mouse.**

There were others, a little more expensive, which the assistant assured me hastily were "better bred".

But I still stuck to my choice and was sure that what the black and white mouse might lack in breeding was more than made up for by the charisma he wore like a crown.

Shona was thrilled when Tiddles, as he was immediately christened, soon demonstrated that he could perform all sorts of tricks, like washing his face with his forepaws when told to, fastidiously combing his white whiskers with tiny claws, then sitting up and begging for a little bit of chocolate before rolling over on his back to have his tummy tickled.

Shona showed off Tiddles to everyone, including our local policeman, who had also kept pet mice when he was a boy and was wistfully allowing Tiddles to travel up the "arm of the law", when his bleeper suddenly started to scream and Tiddles immediately dived for shelter inside the bobbie's blue tunic.

It was an urgent call from Blair Atholl. A Danish tourist's car was stuck in a ditch, so could he come quickly?

The policeman ran to the panda car with Tiddles now nestling down his hairy chest. The tiny mouse was returned some time later, none the worse for his spell "in custody", but apparently the Danish lady had been more than a little concerned about our bobbie's "affliction", as she had called it, when watching him wriggling this way and that.

However, she was full of praise when he put her car back on the road, which all goes to show that the lot of a Highland policeman is not an unhappy one. ∎

A DISH CALLED HAPPINESS

Continued from page 11.

The kitchen trolley, the little hall table, the nest of occasional tables from the lounge and the collapsible picnic table jostled each other for space.

Susan spied crockery which hadn't seen the light of day for years, as well as some of her mother's best china from the display cabinet, and the lawn was littered with crumpled napkins embossed with holly and Merry Christmas.

"Dad!" She ran indoors. "Where are you? Whatever's been going on?"

He was in the kitchen washing up, and by his side, wearing a plastic apron of Susan's, stood Hugh Godwin, wiping and stacking dishes.

"Oh, Susan." Her father looked up, rather guiltily, she thought. "I'm glad you're back, my dear. I can't quite remember where all these things go." His bright tone had a note of mild hysteria in it. She set down her case.

"Dad — look at me! What's all that wreckage outside and why on earth is Hugh having to wipe dishes for you?"

He crossed the room and she noticed he was red-faced and perspiring. There was a smear of raspberry jam near his left eyebrow and froth dripped on to his shirt front as he rubbed his ear shamefacedly.

"It seemed such a good idea at the time," he began, ruefully. "Last Thursday a couple came by and asked if there was anywhere in the village they could get a cup of tea and a cake, so I seized my opportunity and obliged. They were impressed at how very cheap it was, and it got rid of the surplus beautifully.

"Afterwards, I realised tourists coming into Whitmarsh to look at the cathedral often stop here for a look round because the village is so pretty, and . . ."

"But, Dad, you need a licence to do that sort of thing on a regular basis — and we aren't properly equipped! Besides, you'd need help — unless Hugh's going to have a change of career . . . And anyway," she finished faintly, looking round in vain for a chair to collapse in, "I don't think I could face coming home to this every day!"

Hugh's twinkling eyes added to her confusion. He put down the tea-cloth.

"You both look exhausted — allow me." He fetched in two kitchen chairs and sat each of them down solicitously. "There's some tea left in one of these pots. Here you are."

Soothed by his calm, sensible manner, Susan relaxed. "Oh, Dad, I do make it difficult for you, don't I?"

"Nothing of the sort. It's I who've been making it difficult for you — and today I had a taste of my own medicine.

"Those people told their friends, and of course when other people saw teas on the lawn they just came in and joined the rest.

"Saturday was hectic, but today has been impossible — they even came for morning coffee and I hadn't the wit to say I wasn't open yet."

He ran his fingers through his greying hair.

"And they weren't satisfied with cake alone! Hadn't I got toast, they asked — or at least a bit of bread and jam? And scones — I was actually taking them hot from the oven straight to the tables!

"Then the children wanted squash and I ran out, and somebody threw a tantrum. They demanded napkins and straws, and one woman said the bread was like doorsteps, and the butter was too hard to spread properly.

"Then they started asking for poached eggs and omelettes and I just lost my grip . . ."

Susan began to laugh helplessly, and her father's harassed expression melted into a shame-faced grin.

"Bless you, Susan, I wouldn't have blamed you for being furious." He turned to Hugh. "She's a good sport, isn't she?"

"Indeed she is." The warmth of Hugh's smile sent a little quiver through her.

"We'll clear it all up between us, Susan, don't worry about a thing."

"I'll bring in the rest of the crockery," her father said.

Hugh and Susan followed him into the cool garden. Susan sat down.

"What are you doing here anyway, Hugh?" Susan asked as her father picked up the crockery. "Did Dad send up distress signals in oven smoke?"

"As a matter of fact, I called by to see what had happened to you," Hugh said. "You've only been into the shop once this week, and then I was busy dispensing. And you weren't at church this morning, so I dropped by afterwards to see if you were all right."

"You've been here all day?"

"Most of it." He laughed. "Actually, I quite enjoyed it, though I wouldn't like to repeat the experience!"

"Can you — will you stay and have a proper meal with us, Hugh? After all your help, you certainly deserve it."

"No — you're both coming out with me. I insist. The Whitmarsh Arms has an excellent restaurant which is open Sundays. I often go there."

He inclined his head and looked at her quizzically.

"I've never seen you flustered before, Susan, it's given me quite a new insight. And I really missed you calling in at the shop." He stopped then, unsure if he should continue. But the smile in her eyes seemed to spur him on.

"Perhaps next week we could see a film — or drive out to the country and find a nice place to have a cup of tea and a piece of cake?"

"Thank you, Hugh. I'd like that very much."

As he went by, her father observed the blush on Susan's cheeks and the look in Hugh Godwin's eyes. Just the way he used to look at Susan's mother.

And they hadn't even noticed what an incredibly long time it had taken him to collect a few cups and saucers.

He reflected that for the time being, cake baking had rather lost its allure, but no doubt he'd feel better tomorrow. Then he could start practising with wedding cakes. □

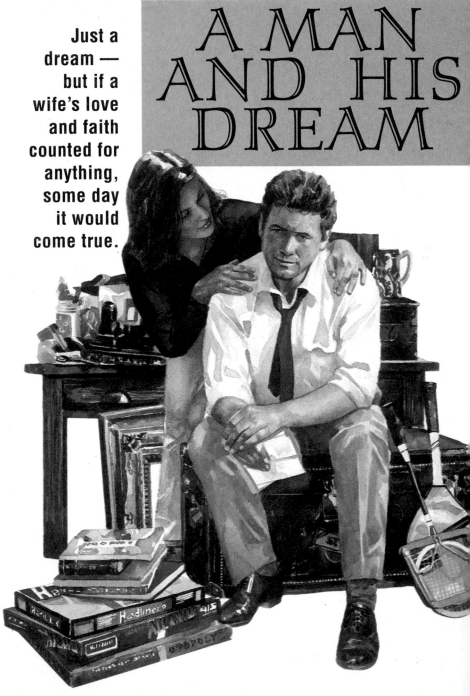

A MAN AND HIS DREAM

Just a dream — but if a wife's love and faith counted for anything, some day it would come true.

Complete Story by DI HARDIE

"YOU'RE sure you can manage, love?" Tim's face was earnest as he asked the question for at least the twelfth time that morning. They were sitting at the kitchen table, Jeremy still in his high-chair, his small face happily smeared with jam, and the lunch dishes still littering the table.

Josie managed a smile. "Of course I can manage. Will you please stop worrying about my side of things and concentrate on your own?"

Tim nodded. She watched as he pushed back his chair and opened the kitchen door. Across the hall she could see their little dining-room, the table covered with sheets of white paper. Tim's sketches, all the exciting designs for wonderful furniture that were suddenly so important.

Tim paused with his hand on the doorknob and leaned back to ruffle Jeremy's mop of fair curls.

"All right. But if you do need me, just give me a shout and . . ."

"Back to your work! Go on!" Josie managed another bright smile. "Go and get a really good selection of designs ready to show Mr Morgan. That's what he's coming for, isn't it?"

Tim went.

The smile faded from Josie's face. She blew out her cheeks in relief and stared at Jeremy. His small face puckered into a grin and he began to hammer his spoon noisily against his mug.

"Oh, no!" Hastily, she took his spoon and pushed his woolly rabbit into his hand. "Not today, darling. I just couldn't take that today."

She wiped the jam from his face, lifted him out of his high-chair and cuddled his warm little body close to hers.

Jeremy chuckled happily and she cuddled him even closer. Darling little Jeremy. It was wrong ever to think of him as a burden, to wonder if things might have been better if he had never happened. Better for Tim, that was.

But it wasn't just Jeremy. Suppose she had never met Tim? Suppose that wonderful summer had never happened? Suppose he had never come to Ockrington to spend the long holiday months sketching and painting?

Surely then he would have gone on with his studies. He would have passed his exams, specialised in the design courses, and revelled in creating his own ideas for furniture. And he would have had a future.

Instead he had met a very ordinary girl named Josie on the quiet bank of a narrow river that lapped its way through a very ordinary little town. He had fallen in love with her and married her.

He believed he had forgotten his dreams. He honestly thought he could push them aside and replace them with new ones, a wife, a baby son, a job at the engineering works in the middle of town.

But the dreams had come back. More and more often she had found him lost in thought, or sketching out some new idea on the first scrap of paper that came to hand, as though afraid that if he did not catch it instantly it would be lost.

A MAN AND HIS DREAM

And there had been problems. His parents had not understood. They had not been unkind, just distant. As if trying to compensate, her family had helped all they could. They had managed to lend the deposit for a little flat, and put in a good word for Tim at the factory.

Tim had been grateful. He had said so often. Perhaps too often. Secretly she had been afraid. It was not good for anyone to feel too indebted. For her to be happy, for Jeremy to be happy, Tim had to be happy, too. Really happy.

Then had come the awful day when he had lost his job. Redundancies were inevitable. The last to come must be the first to go.

She had cried that day, seated on a bench in the park, her head bent unseeing over a magazine.

But Tim loved her. He told her so over and over again that night, his arms wrapped about her, his lips warm on hers. There was no need for tears, he said. He was happy, truly happy. And there was no need to be afraid. He would get another job soon, very soon.

But he didn't.

The days passed. The weeks had drifted into months. She had tried to keep smiling. So had Tim. Bright, false smiles to hide the truth even from each other. And all the time his redundancy money was dwindling away.

"Something will turn up soon. Something good." She had said it so often the words had begun to come stiffly to her lips.

And Tim had smiled reassuringly and gone back to drawing on scraps of paper.

At first she had hardly looked at his designs. Secretly she had always been afraid of them, as though they might come between her and Tim. But, gradually, she had started studying the odd scraps of paper she found.

She tried to understand and appreciate them before tucking them carefully into the drawer where Tim kept his treasured drawing instruments.

TIM had been out of work for almost six months when the letter came. The sight of it, lying white and unexpected on the mat, had been exciting. For so long there had been nothing but the regular bills. She had picked it up and ripped it open before she realised it was addressed to Tim alone. There was to be a reunion. All his old art school friends would be there. The writer hoped Tim would be able to make it.

It had taken her more than a week to persuade him to accept. She had felt it was important that he should.

Things were bad. There was no work in Ockrington. Hope was dying and she didn't know how to keep it alive. She and Tim didn't talk any more. Not the way they used to, looking ahead, having dreams and planning the future. Often she wondered if he regretted marrying her.

That was why it was so important to her that he should go back among his old friends. Truth had to be faced. You couldn't build a worthwhile life without it.

At first Tim refused to even consider going. He had nothing in common now with his old friends. And money was precious.

But in the end he had agreed. He had been gone a whole weekend and from Friday to Sunday she had been filled with a tight, sick apprehension.

Tim would come back. She knew he would come back to the life he had chosen, to her and to Jeremy. But what would he be feeling inside?

She had gone to the station on Sunday dressed in her best and with a bright smile of welcome ready to greet him. But inside she'd been afraid that he would have changed.

And he had.

Out of the crowd he had come running towards her, waving and smiling.

"Josie!" He had folded her in his arms and kissed her. "I've had a wonderful weekend, really wonderful!"

He had taken Jeremy and tucked her arm through his. "Come on. I didn't spend as much as we expected. I'm going to treat you to a tea and a cream cake at the cafe near the bridge. The one we used to go to. Remember?"

He had waited until she was settled in front of a huge cream cake before he would tell her anything.

"It was marvellous, Josie. Everyone was there. We never stopped talking art and design. But, most important, Woody was there. You remember old Woodbridge, the teacher I liked so much, the one who used to give me all the help and encouragement? Well, he seemed really glad to see me and we walked and talked. I told him everything."

"About having a wife and a baby?" Josie stared at the cream cake, a lump in her throat. "And having no job?"

"Everything." Tim squeezed her hand excitedly. "And do you know what? He knows a man who is head of a big furniture manufacturing business. He's going to talk to him, ask if he is ever looking for new designs."

"Tim!" She had clung to his hand across the table, alight with sudden hope. "Tim, honestly?"

"Of course it's only an outside chance. He might have his own

LITTLE DOT

She's a little hard of hearing,
And her eyesight's not so hot,
There's a bit of stiffness in her joints,
But we love our little Dot.

She's getting old and cranky,
And her fur has gone all grey,
But her tail still wags like Billy-o,
When she's called to come and play.

She's been with us since she was small,
And she's brought us so much fun,
We'll love her for all her funny ways,
Until her time has come.
— Mrs T. A., Essex.

A MAN AND HIS DREAM

designers. He mightn't even like my kind of ideas, but . . . it is a hope."

That had been nearly two months ago. Weeks of excitement, of Tim bent intently over sheets of white paper as he transformed rough sketches into beautiful designs.

Then weeks of waiting, and more waiting. Weeks when Tim was still happy and hopeful, but she grew more and more afraid as the bright flame of anticipation flickered lower.

Then the letter came. The notepaper was headed and looked impressive. Mr Derek Morgan of Morgan and White Ltd. was a friend of Mr James Woodbridge. Mr Morgan would be in Ockrington and would like to call. He hoped 6.30 p.m. on Friday would be convenient.

The letter had arrived yesterday morning. And today was Friday.

J OSIE'S eyes flew to the clock. Two o'clock! "And he'll be here at half-past six!" She gave Jeremy a last cuddle and put him back in his high-chair.

She shook her head firmly as he clung to her. "You must be good. You must. I've got so much to do I'll never be ready in time."

Go shopping, finish cleaning the windows, polish the sitting-room floor, look out and wash the cream and green coffee set that had been Aunt Marie's wedding present, press Tim's trousers, check her best dress for spots . . . the list seemed endless . . .

She almost ran all the way to the shops. And all the way back. Tim's head was still bent over his designs when she peeped in again.

At half-past four she made him a cup of coffee. The sitting-room floor was polished, the windows were cleaned, and the cream and green china had been washed and dried. She would have liked a cup of coffee herself. It would have been an excuse to sit down for a few minutes, but the clock ticked relentlessly on.

At half-past five she bathed Jeremy, and at six o'clock, fed and sleepy, she took him in to kiss Tim goodnight.

"Six o'clock and all's well." She tried to sound calm and cheerful. "Now perhaps you had better get tidy. Mr Morgan could be early."

But he wasn't early. At six-thirty exactly she stood beside Tim in the middle of the sitting-room and drew a deep sigh of relief. The flat was as perfect as she could make it, not a muddle, not a baby toy, not even an old newspaper in sight.

Jeremy had fallen asleep the moment he had been laid in his cot. She had even had time to put on a little make-up and coax her hair into curls round her forehead the way Tim liked it.

Tim brought his designs and laid them on the coffee table, and they sat side by side on the settee, waiting.

At a quarter to seven Tim squeezed her hand. "Of course, he may not like my ideas," he said quietly.

"He will. He'll love them." She was proud of the confidence in her voice and she held his hand tightly as they fell silent again.

"I don't even know what kind of furniture Morgan and White make."

20

The hands of the clock had crawled round to seven. "I should have asked Woody, I suppose. I didn't think. I was just so pleased . . ."

"It doesn't matter." She tried to sound casual, but the strange, tidy silence of the flat was beginning to make her edgy. "He'll be able to see that you're good at designing. He'll tell you what he really wants."

Tim smiled and nodded and they were silent again.

At eight o'clock Jeremy began to cry. It was a long time before she could get him to sleep again. When she did go back, Tim was sitting, waiting silently. At nine o'clock she made coffee and they sat side by side and drank it in silence.

At quarter to ten Tim gathered his designs and took them back to the dining-room.

"He probably only said he would call to please Woody." His voice was flat. "He probably wasn't really interested . . ."

Jeremy was crying again. She went back to him. By the time she had settled him, Tim had gone to bed. Later, when she lay down beside him, he said nothing. There seemed nothing to say.

In the darkness she cried gently for a long time before she fell asleep.

Tim was up before she was awake next morning. There was a note on the kitchen table.

Don't worry, Josie. Gone for a walk. I wanted to be alone, that's all. I love you. Tim.

She made a pot of tea and sat down at the kitchen table and drank cup after cup. In his high-chair Jeremy splattered himself with cereal and chuckled gleefully as he tossed spoonfuls across the floor. It didn't matter. Suddenly nothing mattered.

The cereal all gone, Jeremy cried. She gave him bread and jam and he wiped it round his face and then threw it on the floor and cried again.

She took him from his high-chair and settled him into his playpen in the cold tidiness of the sitting-room. Building bricks, saucepan lids, the woolly rabbit, everything she could think of, she tossed in to amuse him.

Then she sat down on the settee. She wanted to cry but there didn't seem to be any tears left. Instead she sat listlessly, watching Jeremy.

Chuckling with delight, he balanced himself on his chubby little legs

NIGHT SKY

*Wish upon
a falling star
Perhaps
it will come true,
Careful
not to waste it,
Shooting stars
are few.*

*Magic
surrounds it
Wonderment
and awe,
Excited
emotions
You've never
felt before.*

*Quickly
make a wish
Before
it's out of sight,
Fulfilment
may be granted
During this
forthcoming night.*

— Mrs B. E., Tyne & Wear.

and heaved his toys one at a time as far as he could throw them.

The ring at the door startled her. But it meant nothing. Tim had his own key. It was probably someone selling brushes. She went to the front door.

The woman was elderly, with white hair neatly set back into deep waves, clothes that were quiet but well cut and expensive. She looked pleasant, but brisk, efficient and businesslike.

"Mrs Watson?" She held out her hand. "My name is White. Madeleine White.

"I'd like to see your husband."

"I'm sorry. He's out . . ."

The words tailed off. White? The name was beginning to mean something.

"Oh, what a pity." She looked genuinely disappointed. "My husband, Derek Morgan, made an appointment to see him last night but I'm afraid he went down with a bad attack of migraine. They usually put him out of action for a day or two so I'm driving him home today.

"Well . . ." She smiled politely. "I'm so sorry. I'm afraid I couldn't get a message to your husband. I only got into Ockrington late last night myself.

"Derek and I are partners in the business, you see. We started it before we were married. We usually split the business trips between us, and we were to meet here and stay at the Royal Hotel overnight."

She paused. "I just thought perhaps, as Derek had promised Mr Woodbridge, I might glance through your husband's designs myself before we left. Still, it can't be helped . . ."

Josie stood very still. Her dress was old and faded, and her slippers were down-at-heel. Behind her the room doors were open. In the kitchen there were dirty dishes on the table and cereal, bread and jam on the floor. In the sitting-room, Jeremy, smeared and grubby, was still tossing toys.

"I'll show you his designs," she said shyly.

She closed the front door and led the way into the dining-room. It was tiny, but at least it was clean and tidy. Quickly Josie brought out the designs from the drawer and spread them across the table.

"Furniture is something we all live with." She realised she was repeating Tim's words as he had gone over his designs with her. "It's a big part of our lives.

"Just as every person is different, so Tim feels the furniture they surround themselves with should be different. Quiet and simple for some, bold and extravagant for others. It wouldn't necessarily have to be expensive, not if the designs were right, wasting no material, keeping the labour to an absolute minimum . . ."

She broke off, suddenly self-conscious, her cheeks flushed. "But perhaps you'd rather have a look through them on your own."

She mopped the kitchen floor, cleared the table and washed the dishes. Through the open dining-room door she could see Madeleine White studying the designs.

She cleaned Jeremy's hands and face and gathered up the toys.

"Please. Don't fuss on my account."

Suddenly Josie was aware of Madeleine White in the doorway, watching her. Her smile was friendly.

"Children are happier when they are dirty," she said. "I should know. I had four, and when mine were young I never managed to keep any of them clean for more than five minutes at a time."

Then Josie heard it — Tim's key in the lock!

He walked over and put his arm round her. Then he turned to look at their visitor.

Madeleine White stepped forward, her hand outstretched.

"Tim Weston? I'm Madeleine White, the other half of Morgan and White. Your wife has been showing me your sketches."

Josie saw Tim's eyes widen in wonder and delight as he followed Madeleine White into the dining-room. Josie lifted the baby and went after them.

"Tim, I like your designs." Madeleine flicked lightly through them again as she spoke. "I like your ideas and I like your style. I'm sure Derek would, too, but . . ."

She shook her head. "We never buy designs from outsiders. We have our own. They work hand in hand with the production managers. They know all the practical problems of the shop floor."

There was a long silence. Josie did not look at Tim. She only cuddled Jeremy tighter, fighting back the disappointment that brought tears to her eyes.

"I'm sorry." Tim's voice was subdued. "I'm sure Mr Woodbridge didn't realise. It was good of you to waste your time. Thank you for coming."

"Not at all." She smiled at him. "It's entirely up to you. If you are interested in joining our staff I have a feeling we'll find a place for you. Of course it would depend on my husband too, but I think I can speak for him. You would have a chance to learn the practical side of things. I think you would enjoy it."

She looked at Josie and her eyes were kind. "I'm afraid our factory is at Plessbridge. It's about seventy miles from here. It would mean moving house, leaving Ockrington."

Josie stared. Hope and disappointment . . . now hope again. She felt dazed.

"Mrs White," she said quietly, "it's up to Tim. If it's what he wants, then I shall be happy."

"Tim, I have a feeling we have a future together," Madeleine White smiled at Josie and touched Jeremy's cheek. "I may be old-fashioned but I always have faith in a man with a happy family behind him. I think you are very lucky."

Josie felt Tim close to her. He took Jeremy from her and put his arm round her shoulder.

"I am," he said fervently. "I am so very lucky." □

A Recipe

E DITH PETTIFER held up the bootees she had just finished and examined them critically. Well, they might sell at tomorrow's fête. There was always the possibility that someone in Millbridge had a baby with size 12 feet.

Still, it seemed most unlikely. Edith sighed and shook her head. Knitting had never been one of her particular talents. Business studies, shorthand and typing, yes. When it came to running an office almost single-handed, she was in her element.

But the gifts that had earned her a living for over 30 years couldn't help her to win acceptance into the little community here.

Perhaps everyone had been right, she thought sadly. Perhaps it was a mistake to uproot yourself in retirement.

"You mark my words, Edie," her sister had said gloomily, "you'll regret it. City plants don't do in country air."

It was true in a way, Edith supposed. When she had accepted voluntary redundancy from Marchant's, and bought the small cottage down here, it had seemed such a good idea. A new start at 55 years of age. New home, new friends, new way of life.

But as Ruby had forecast, things were never as easy as you imagined.

Oh, her immediate neighbours were friendly enough. And she had met more people when she joined the St Oswald's Ladies Guild, but it was difficult to believe she would ever really "belong" there. All the other women were so — well, so very good at everything!

24

For Love

Complete Story by SARAH BURKHILL

Nearly everyone had supplied the most beautifully knitted garments or stuffed toys for tomorrow's fête. Most of them had made jam or preserves to sell, and some had grown lovely pot plants for the garden stall.

Edith frowned at the white bootees and dropped them into the bin.

That settled, Edith wandered into the little kitchen and prepared to tackle her next problem.

Mrs Wood, the Guild president, had asked everyone to bake something for the tea-room they were having in the church hall.

Edith searched through the recipe book which had been supplied with her new cooker. Baking was another thing she had no great talent for, though of course there had never been much need for it before. Living alone, it was easier just to have a shop-bought cake than bake one herself.

Still, it didn't look too difficult according to this recipe book. She had decided on shortbread, and carefully mixed all the ingredients as shown in the colour pictures.

But what came out of the oven twenty minutes later didn't look at all like the colour pictures. Edith frowned at the little squares laid out on a tin rack to cool. Carefully she attempted to bite through one, and there ensued a battle between the shortbread and her National Health dentures. Before the former could claim victory, Edith abandoned the fight.

It was too late to begin anything else now. She would get up very early in the morning and have another go, she decided, as she went up to her bedroom.

Tossing and turning in bed, Edith peered around her. Oh, she loved this little room with its sloping ceiling and latticed windows! She loved the whole cottage and its tiny patch of garden.

She loved the village, too, and the way of life so different from the bustle of town. If only she could just — just fit in better, she thought, everything could be so nice.

Edith turned over to her right side as St Oswald's clock struck one. The cake — she had forgotten about it for a moment. What was she going to do? She couldn't turn up with nothing tomorrow, it was unthinkable.

She turned the pillows over and moved to her left side, where she could see the luminous hands of her bedside alarm. Twenty past two, she must have dozed off.

She tried lying on her back again, the cake looming large, a symbol of success or failure.

And then, as St Oswald's clock struck three, Edith smiled.

A RECIPE FOR LOVE

It was perfectly simple really. She would buy a cake! There was a nice little home bakery at the top of Johnston Street. She would get something suitable there, and no-one need ever know.

WILSON'S BAKERY was really much too grand an establishment for a place like Millbridge, Edith thought the next morning. She had gazed at the window display many a time but had never ventured over the threshold.

The array inside was even more tempting than that in the window. But in here a neat little price tag was attached to each item. Edith frowned at them in dismay.

"Yes, m'dear, what can I do for you?" Sam Wilson himself beamed jovially from behind his well-stocked counter. "I'd like a — cake. I think," she said rather hesitantly, figures adding and subtracting in her head.

"I've a nice chocolate cake this morning," Sam Wilson said helpfully. "Very popular, they are."

She looked at the price and shook her head.

"No, I don't think so. Perhaps something a little less — less —"

"Gingerbread," the baker suggested.

Edith examined it for a moment. "Well, maybe a little more —" Her eyes darted about the shop.

"I know," Sam Wilson said, "I've got just the thing for you. A piece of cake you might say!"

He laughed uproariously and disappeared into the back shop, returning a moment later with a delicate sponge creation.

"There! What about that?

"The honey cake, Mark 1. It's a new recipe for me. I'll let you have it cheap, seeing that it's a trial for me, really."

"Is it all right?" Edith said timidly. It certainly looked lovely.

"All right? All right?" Sam Wilson echoed. "Why of course it's all right. Nothing comes out of my oven that isn't all right!"

"Yes, yes, I'm sure," Edith said quickly. "And I'll take it. Thank you very much."

At home, she transferred the honey cake into one of her tins, collected the apron Mrs Wood had advised bringing along, and set off for the church hall. Now that the cake problem was solved, Edith's mind was free to worry about her other morning duties. Mrs Eckerslie had suggested she help on the jams and preserves stall and Edith's heart jumped at the thought of it.

What if she charged the wrong prices, or — or dropped something. Jam would make a terrible mess. It would get stamped everywhere if someone stood on it, and knowing her luck . . .

"Miss Pettifer, what a lovely cake," the vicar's wife said admiringly when she deposited it in the kitchen.

"Now will you keep one slice aside from the tea-room's and mark it with your name?" Mrs Douglas said. "After all the effort people have put in, we thought we'd make things more interesting and have a 'best cake' contest afterwards."

Edith stared at her. "You're going to — to do — what?"

"A contest, dear," Mrs Douglas said kindly. "The vicar himself will judge the cakes, and we'll have —"

"Oh, but I don't think so!" Edith said frantically. "I mean, I'd rather not have my cake — er —"

"Nonsense!" Mrs Douglas beamed. "From the look of it, I'd say you have a very good chance. And it'll be fun, won't it?"

Edith felt a thrill of sheer horror. In fact, she worried so much about the possibility of winning that she had no time to worry about serving on the jam stall, and she didn't make even one little mistake.

Oh, please don't let it win, she prayed silently as the fête drew to a close and the vicar took his place on the platform.

One by one, Mr Douglas tasted all the delicacies before him, and Edith's state of anxiety increased by the minute.

It couldn't win. Surely it couldn't! Mrs Tomkins always won the cake contests. Mrs Tomkins always won everything, come to that. Edith had heard one or two of the ladies muttering about it, and their comments seemed rather uncharitable.

Mrs Tomkins was standing beside Edith now, smiling superciliously and radiating confidence as the vicar tasted the last piece of cake.

"And the winner is —"

Oh, no. Oh, no! A squeak of tension escaped from Edith and Mrs Tomkins gave her a sharp glance.

"— is Miss Edith Pettifer for her honey cake!"

Edith felt faint as a wave of applause lapped around her.

She would move, that's what she'd do. She would sell up the cottage and go back to the city. She would face Ruby's "I told you so," and admit that her elder, much-married sister was right as usual.

That would be better — anything would be better — than facing this illustrious band of women when they found out she had cheated in the St Oswald's Fête Cake Contest!

"Miss Pettifer, I didn't suspect such hidden talents!" Dorothy Dunn gushed.

"Well, I — er —"

"About time somebody new about this place took the honours," Beth White muttered, casting meaningful glances at the outraged Mrs Tomkins.

"But — but you see, I didn't know there was to be a contest," Edith squeaked. "I thought it was just a Sale of Work."

"Well, if that wasn't your best effort, I'd like to see a cake you really try with," Mrs Eckerslie said. "It looked simply delicious. You must give me the recipe."

"Oh, but I can't!" Edith was lost for words. "It's — I mean — that is to say —"

"It's an old family secret, I expect." Effie Middleton nodded sagely. "Just like my gingerbread. Don't worry, dear." She patted Edith's arm.

A RECIPE FOR LOVE

"We shan't press you into revealing the magic ingredients."

Edith sank deeper into despair as the conversation went on. Oh, what if it ever came out? Why, she'd never hold up her head in Millbridge again!

A S it happened, though, Edith Pettifer's secret was safe. Throughout her life in Millbridge, through her rise to secretary of St Oswald's Guild and then to President, not one member ever suspected that her success was based on such trickery and deceit.

Until last week, that is. For that was when Edith, retiring after her fifth consecutive year as President, chose to confess her guilt.

Dora Greenaway, the woman she'd confessed to and the guild's newest member, looked at her disbelievingly.

"You mean — you mean to say you conned all the old biddies into thinking —" She choked back a laugh and Edith smiled.

"So you see, my dear, you mustn't worry about not being able to keep up with the others. Everyone has different talents, and I'm sure in time you'll find you have as much to contribute to the community as anyone else."

Dora shook her head. "I must say I still can't believe it. You're always so — so efficient and competent. I thought you could do just about anything you wanted to."

"Well, so I can — now," Edith said complacently. "After that dreadful business of the honey cake, I just had to learn, didn't I?

"And, of course, I had a very good teacher," she added more modestly.

Dora Greenaway finished clearing up the cups and saucers from the retiring President's tea party.

"I'm just surprised no-one ever found out," she said after a moment. "I didn't think it possible to keep secrets in a place like Millbridge."

Edith sniffed. "Well, actually, one person did find out. It turned out that the baker was Mrs Tomkins' cousin, so when he found out she'd been beaten by a honey cake, he sort of — put two and two together.

"It was very awkward," Edith went on slowly. "In fact, it led to me being blackmailed! Blackmailed, if you please!

"Still, things didn't —"

Edith broke off, her eyes going to the window and a smile softening her face.

"Oh, here's my Sam now — come to collect me," she said hurriedly. "I'd better get off now, dear."

"Thanks," Dora called after her. "For telling me, I mean."

"Not at all," Edith said. "I'm sure honesty is the best policy most of the time, but there are occasions when things can work out better with just a little lie."

"There's just one thing," Dora said.

"Yes?"

"You said he blackmailed you — how?"

Edith Wilson smiled. "Why, into marrying him, of course," she said and left, softly closing the door behind her. ☐

AUNT AGATHA'S FINEST HOUR

Everyone was amazed that she of all people had grown the prizewinning bloom — everyone except the little girl who shared the secret of her success.

M Y Aunt Agatha was very different from other people. At least, she was the only person in our family who thought of tying a sprig of rowan to my baby sister's cot, so that she wouldn't be stolen by the fairies.

My mother was embarrassed at the time, but she didn't object. Aunt Agatha with her black hair and strikingly-handsome, dark eyes could look quite intimidating if she was thwarted, and my mother had always let her have her own way.

People in our village had never forgotten the time Aunt Agatha foretold the winner of the Derby simply by looking at the leaves in my gran's cup; and if anyone was afflicted by warts, they always asked her to cure them. And somehow, she always did.

In my first memories of Aunt Agatha she was never far away from her

29

AUNT AGATHA'S FINEST HOUR

cat, Willie. But like Aunt Agatha, Willie had grown older and had recently passed on to a happier world. Now, although Aunt Agatha herself would never admit it, I suspected that she was lonely without him.

She certainly was different, and more interesting to me than Aunt Moira, my mother's other unmarried sister, who always won first prize at the W.I. for her sponge sandwich. And a lot more interesting than my friend, Amy, with whom I disagreed on almost every subject you could mention.

"Your Aunt Agatha is a witch," Amy declared one day. "Everybody says so!"

"Well then," I retorted, giving her long, fair ponytail a tug, "I'll ask her to turn you into a frog. Not that anyone would notice the difference!"

When I got home from school that afternoon, I found my mother having tea with Aunt Agatha and Aunt Moira. It was the year the vicar had received the bad news about the church roof, and great plans were afoot in the village to raise the money to repair it.

There were going to be fairs, a miracle play, a donkey derby and a fireworks display organised by the vicar.

Altogether we were all really quite pleased about the state of the church roof. It looked as if there would be more fun in our village than we'd had for a long time!

I helped myself to a biscuit and listened. Aunt Moira was explaining to the others her own fund-raising idea.

I should mention that Aunt Moira was not only the sponge cake queen of the W.I., but she also had the greenest fingers in the village, always carrying off half the prizes at the annual horticultural show. So, of course, her fund-raising idea was bound to have something to do with flowers.

"I thought we might organise a Sunflower Race," she suggested. "You see, you sell everyone a giant sunflower seed for, say, fifty pence, and they get other people to sponsor them and pay so much an inch according to how tall the flower eventually grows."

My mother and Aunt Agatha listened with expressionless faces. You could see they thought Aunt Moira had gone completely round the bend.

"Don't you see, it would make about as much money as a jumble sale, and it would be fun, too," Aunt Moira cried eagerly, her little, round face turning rather pink.

"The vicar could measure the plants at the end, and we'd have a little prize for the winner. The bigger your sunflower, the more you'd make for the church fund."

No-one said anything, so she turned to me.

"Don't you think it would be fun, Lucy?"

"Yes, I do," I agreed, feeling sorry for Aunt Moira. "I expect the children at school would join in, although I don't think they'd want to pay as much as fifty pence for one seed."

"Their parents would help, I'm sure," Aunt Moira said briskly. "It would be something like a sponsored walk, but it will be a sponsored grow."

Then, annoyed by Aunt Agatha's amused smile, she added tartly, "I don't suppose you'll be taking part, Agatha, you're not much for gardening, are you, dear?"

"Me?" Aunt Agatha was obviously nettled. "Of course I will. I'll grow the biggest sunflower of the lot."

I suppose it was then that the Sunflower Race turned into not just a fund-raising event, but a contest between Aunt Moira and Aunt Agatha.

As I said, Aunt Moira was always among the prizewinners at the flower show. Her garden had a smooth, well-groomed lawn and neatly-pruned roses and shrubs. Aunt Agatha's garden was a jungle of old apple trees, overgrown, sweetly-scented shrub roses, buttercups, honeysuckle and daisies.

It was a paradise for butterflies and I loved to lie in the long grass under the trees on warm summer afternoons.

WELL, thanks to Aunt Moira's determination, the Sunflower Race turned out to be a success. Most people bought seeds and planted them, and as the plants began to shoot up, Amy and I often walked round the village, checking on their progress.

Amy and I measured ours often, but tantalisingly they both remained exactly the same size as each other, no matter how tall they grew.

Aunt Moira had generously bought up the last of the seeds and planted them all at the end of her garden where they stood like a small crowd of little green men. They looked healthy and luxuriant, thanks to her assiduous attention.

Although she told my mother, "Of course, it would never do for me to win as I'm the organiser," nobody believed a word of it. Aunt Moira fully expected to win.

But she hadn't reckoned on Aunt Agatha.

In the course of my regular sunflower inspections, I didn't overlook Aunt Agatha's. She had planted her seed in the garden close by the front door, and I persuaded her to let me measure it one day. As I suspected, it definitely was taller than anyone else's. Much taller.

Then one day as I passed by on my way home from school, I noticed Aunt Agatha in her garden. She was standing in front of the sunflower, and I felt sure I heard her say, "Come on, Willie, you can do it!"

Willie, I thought, feeling puzzled. My aunt's enormous black tom cat? But he'd been dead a few months now.

"Hello, Aunt Agatha," I called.

My aunt spun round, obviously surprised and a little put out to find me there.

"Oh, it's you, Lucy," she said. "Come in."

Over a glass of delicious home-made lemonade, my aunt talked about why she'd planted her sunflower there by the front door.

"It was Willie's favourite spot." She smiled reminiscently. "He loved to lie snoozing there in the sun on that big cushion of catmint. You see, when he got too old to get about much, he could still watch everything going on in the street from there."

She gave a little sniff, and her eyes were suspiciously bright.

"So when he died, I thought it was just right for his last resting place. Poor old Willie."

Aunt Agatha was a long time looking in the fridge for more ice cubes. I could tell she was still missing Willie badly.

"Most people would think I was silly, I expect," she said, turning round, "but perhaps you'll understand, Lucy. I thought I'd plant my sunflower seed there in memory of Willie." She smiled suddenly. "I expect that's why it's growing so big."

I smiled, too. The idea of Willie growing into a flower appealed to me considerably. And what a flower! Tall and strong and splendid it was.

As I walked home, I thought about Willie. There had been something strange and mysterious about him as he went about his own private concerns in the village, seeming to be everywhere and nowhere.

There is little doubt that if Aunt Agatha had been a witch, which of course she wasn't, Willie was just the sort of cat she would have had.

But of course, even Willie had grown old, and now she was alone without her faithful companion and friend. Poor Aunt Agatha.

WHEN I got home my mother sent me up to Pengellys' Farm for some eggs. Mrs Pengelly was busy feeding the hens when I came into the yard.

There were nearly always kittens at Pengellys' Farm. There was an official cat population of four, but Mrs Pengelly had a soft heart, and visiting strays and new arrivals awaiting kind homes made it difficult to keep track of all the cats there.

"Blackie's had her first litter of kittens," she told me. "She's in the barn."

In a box lined with an old blanket I found Blackie and two kittens. I stroked her gently, and she eyed me watchfully as I extended a cautious finger to touch her babies.

One was a small, sleepy replica of herself, black with a white bib and diminutive white paws. The other, bigger and entirely black, was suckling away with single-minded tenacity as if he was in a tearing hurry to grow up.

I looked at this furry scrap with growing excitement. Tiny as he was, there was something oddly familiar about him.

"Going to be a big 'un, he is." Mrs Pengelly had come in behind me.

"Could you keep him for me?" I asked eagerly. "I would like him as a present for my Aunt Agatha. It's a secret."

"Sure I will, Lucy. I'm only too glad to know there's a home for him. And he does bear a resemblance to your Aunt's old cat, I must say." She laughed. "Not that it's surprising really."

I knew what she meant. Our village had an exceptionally large

32

population of black cats. In the old country phrase, Willie had cast his image about a bit, but I'd never seen any of his many descendants touch him for size and sheer personality.

Obviously no ordinary cat could console Aunt Agatha. Was it too much to hope that Blackie had produced another Willie?

"Come round and see the kitten any time you like," Mrs Pengelly said, handing me the eggs. "He'll be ready to leave his mother quite soon."

During the summer holidays the sunflowers started to open their yellow petals, each brown centre like a big treacle tart, and the vicar set a date for the judging.

Aunt Moira was too proud to admit to her curiosity about the final height of Aunt Agatha's sunflower, so she couldn't just go round there to see for herself.

When she asked me in an off-hand manner if I had any idea who was likely to be the winner of the Sunflower Race, I knew what was on her mind.

I answered truthfully that most of the sunflowers around the village seemed to be much the same height as far as I could tell from my round of inspections.

She smiled, until I added casually, "Except Aunt Agatha's, of course."

"Why 'of course', child?"

"Well," I said, playing it cool, "the last time I measured it, it was about eight feet tall."

Registering shock, Aunt Moira shut the door with a bang.

I left quickly and went on up to the farm to see the rapidly-growing kitten. Already he was twice as big as his brother, and I could hardly wait to see Aunt Agatha's face when I handed him over.

I HAD decided to give Aunt Agatha the kitten on the day that the vicar judged the Sunflower Race, so that morning I went up to the farm with a cat basket.

The hens were rushing about excitedly as I walked into the yard and I was stunned to see huge yellow sunflower heads scattered everywhere on the ground.

When I turned to Mrs Pengelly for an explanation, she shrugged.

"Your Aunt Moira just brought them up today for the hens. According to her, they'd been broken off in the night."

"But how? It's the judging today."

"Freak storm, she said."

Puzzled, I picked up the kitten, and he purred, clinging to my hand. After my many visits, I really thought he knew me.

"Come on," I said, putting him gently into the basket, "it's time to go home." And I set off towards Aunt Agatha's.

When I passed Aunt Moira's house she was in her front garden.

"Auntie," I called, "whatever happened to your sunflowers? I've just been up to the farm and seen them."

AUNT AGATHA'S FINEST HOUR

"Oh," her voice was casual, "they got snapped off in the night. Must have been a freak storm."

I looked at her smooth lawn, sparkling with only the merest hint of dew, and at the perfect border, with never a flower out of place.

"A storm, Aunt Moira?" I queried. "Are you sure?"

"What else could it have been? Don't ask so many questions, child." She flushed under my gaze.

"Still, no matter. The vicar will get his contribution to the fund just the same. I'll see to that. Don't let me keep you, dear, you'll want to see who wins, won't you?"

I walked on thoughtfully. Aunt Moira knew perfectly well who would win. She had known since yesterday when I told her the final measurement of Aunt Agatha's giant sunflower, and she must have realised that not one of her own sunflowers came near it for size.

I thought of those neatly-severed flower heads scattered around the farm yard for the hens, and I knew. There had been a freak storm all right, when Aunt Moira had faced the fact that she, the expert gardener, was about to be beaten by Aunt Agatha of all people. She had done the only possible thing she could to save her face and her reputation.

WHEN I got to Aunt Agatha's garden, several people were standing by the fence, watching the vicar flourishing his tape measure.

"An outright winner," he told Aunt Agatha. "This really is a most exceptional flower. Your sponsors will have to dig deep!"

The bystanders raised a small cheer.

I stooped and put the cat basket on the path, and carefully opened the door. The kitten hesitantly walked out, stretched and looked all around him. Then, with a little shake, he set off up the path towards the front door.

He reached the old catmint plant that Willie had loved so well, and without any hesitation, he climbed unsteadily on top of it, curled up and went straight off to sleep in the shade of Aunt Agatha's sunflower.

The vicar was still talking, but I don't think Aunt Agatha heard a word of what he said. She was looking happier than I'd seen her look for a long time, and I felt sure it was nothing to do with winning the Sunflower Race.

"What will you call him, Aunt Agatha?" I asked her later, as we sat together in her kitchen.

Aunt Agatha was stroking the kitten's smooth black head.

"I shall call him Phoebus," she said.

"Phoebus, Auntie?"

"Yes. You see, Lucy, in ancient times Phoebus was the Sun god, and sunflowers were his emblem, so I think it's quite a good choice, don't you?"

Phoebus opened one eye, and purred softly. Obviously, it was all right with him. □

34

Night Flight from Athens

When the wheels touched the runway, one couple came down to earth in more ways than one.

Complete Story by PHYLLIS DEMAINE

S AMANTHA BROWN walked through the lounge of Athens Airport carefully carrying two cups of coffee. She was tall and slim and she seemed to weave her way through the other travellers and their luggage with an effortless sway of her hips.

When she came to yet another sleeping-bag-cocooned figure, her long legs, tanned to a golden brown by the Greek sun, stepped effortlessly over it.

She felt, but disdainfully ignored, the gaze of those men whose eyes followed her progress. One, braver than the others, smiled into her face, but she chose not to see him.

She wasn't wearing make-up. They had been travelling all day from the island and, on reaching the airport, she had quickly cleansed her face, preferring its naked appearance to the mask of tired mascara and smeared lipstick.

But smudges of sleepiness darkened her eyes, lending them an air of mystery which the lowered lashes did nothing to dispel. Even scrubbed clean, with crumpled clothes and her features blurred with lack of sleep, Samantha Brown was beautiful.

Mark's eyes gleamed a welcome as they focused on her, and his tan

35

emphasised their blueness. Where the wings of hair by his temples had begun to silver, the sun had bleached them further, and as he smiled, Samantha's heart missed a beat.

He was so handsome and, oh, how she loved him!

Two glorious weeks they'd had together. Every minute, waking and sleeping, filled with contentment, love and laughter, sun and sea. The glow from the day's sun worship would merge with the glow from the wine and the moonlight until they lay under the cool sheets listening to the shush of the waves 'way down below the villa.

It had all been so perfect and now it was over.

Soon their flight would be called and in a few hours they would be back in the grey, damp dawn of England. Back to the lives they had left behind.

A tear pricked her eye as she took the seat Mark had been guarding for her. She sipped the coffee, now tepid, and stared into the future.

They had been so close, so happy together, why did it have to end? But she knew it must. In a very little while now they would go back to their own lives.

He to his office with its meetings, discussions and business lunches, she to her desk with its typewriter and overflowing filing trays. She usually managed a sandwich and a snatched cup of tea, before shopping quickly in her lunch-break.

Oh, they would meet, coming together like strangers, friendly strangers who knew the details of each other's lives but shared so little of them.

TWO weeks they'd had. Was that all their love meant? Two weeks when they belonged to each other? "Thanks, Sam." Mark's voice cut across her thoughts. "I needed that." He sipped his coffee.

"Won't be long now." His finger touched a strand of hair which lay damply on her neck. "Sorry about this, but day-time flights are so much more expensive. Are you very tired?"

Samantha shook her head angrily, turning her face away.

He means I look tired, she thought, old and tired. Thirty-nine is no age for sleeping in airport lounges.

Impatiently she ran her fingers through the curls of her recently-permed hair. She had thought it would be easier to manage on the long journey but now she saw that it looked young and ridiculous.

She took a comb from her bag, dragging it through her hair ferociously, then pulling the curls back from her face, she stuck in two slides.

"I liked it like that," Mark said mildly, wondering what had angered her.

"It's been a great holiday, hasn't it, love?" he went on, trying to recapture the wonder of it all. "But I expect you'll be glad to get back to the kids.

"I hope they'll like the presents we brought, your mother too. If it hadn't been for her . . ." Mark left the sentence unfinished.

Mum would be waiting to hear everything, to share their happiness. I mustn't let her down, Samantha thought.

She remembered her earlier elation as she'd threaded her way back to Mark and laughed regretfully, somewhere deep inside, for the Samantha that might have been.

"I'm 39, I've been married 15 years, I've got two children." She sighed. "I'm just 'good old Sam.' The holiday's over."

Mark was getting to his feet, sorting the bags, tucking their tickets into the pocket of the flight bag which bulged with bottles of wine.

"Come on, Sam, time to check in."

Samantha slung her bag over her shoulder but continued to sit there. Mark took her hands, pulling her to her feet tenderly, sensing her unhappiness.

As they faced each other he looked into her eyes.

"Do you know something, Samantha Brown? I think I'm in love with you. I'd nearly forgotten how it felt, but now I remember, and I don't think I'll ever forget again."

He bent his head and kissed her surprised lips. "It's been a great holiday, worth every penny. No matter what, they can't take that away from us."

Samantha fell into step beside him, joining her hands to his on the luggage trolley, resting her head against his arm.

Sam Brown, 39, nothing much to shout about, but with a husband who loved her and told her so, right there, in front of everyone, in the middle of Athens Airport.

"No, Mark, they can't ever take that away from us," she whispered. □

ONLY

*Only a special look is all I ask for
Only a little hope is in each prayer,
One secret glimpse of Paradise I yearn for,
To wake from my dreams and find you standing there.*

*Sleep has a way of promising me starlight
Then stepping aside to show me empty skies,
How can I go on living in a dreamworld
When there's nothing more than reality in your eyes?*

*Only a while ago I felt your whispers
warm and caressing in a tender song,
But your words are like waves that wash upon the seashore
Beckoning — drowning my senses — then are gone . . .*

— Ms P. S., Middlesex.

THE CLUE TO

**Breaking-up
is easy.
It's putting
it all back
together
again
that's
hard . . .**

IT all began when the treasurer of the Shelby Tennis and Recreation Club dropped his bombshell. "No outing!" Walter Reilly exclaimed indignantly. "But we always have an annual outing!"

"I'm sorry, but the new tariff from the coach-hire people has just come in," the treasurer went on. "And with two pounds fourteen pence in the outing fund, we'd be lucky to get as far as Victoria Park."

There was silence for a moment and then Joan Morris piped up. "Well, why don't we do something different this year? Actually, I've got an idea I'd like to put to you . . ." she suggested brightly.

Allan looked at his watch and groaned audibly. Joan's ideas had been known to take anything up to three hours, and he'd been anxious all afternoon to get his car back from the garage.

"It'll be closed," he complained. "The garage closes early on a Saturday and it'll be Monday before I get it back. Couldn't we just sneak out and . . ."

"Ssh!" I told him. "This might be quite interesting."

It was interesting. In fact, as Joan's ideas go, it was definitely one of the better ones.

"A rally treasure hunt?" Walter Reilly was repeating doubtfully. "What d'you mean, a treasure hunt?"

Joan beamed, and burst into full flow. It was perfectly simple, she explained. One of her friends had tried it last year.

Someone was appointed to set a trail of clues around the area, each one leading on to the next, and the first car to reach the end of the trail won the treasure.

"Humph! Don't think much of that," Walter objected. "What about the

HAPPINESS . . .

Complete Story by SARAH BURKHILL

members without cars?"

"Nothing to worry about," Joan assured him. "We work in pairs — driver and navigator — so there should be enough drivers to cope."

Walter was not to be assured so easily.

"Well then, what are you having for treasure?" he went on. "Two pounds fourteen pence is hardly worth hunting for."

That's where Joan played her trump card. She suggested an entrance fee of £1 per person, half of which would provide the prize, the other half going into the outing funds for next year's trip.

That convinced them. Walter's hand was first to shoot up when we took a vote on the treasure hunt, and then all that remained to decide was date, time and organising committee.

"Why can't they hurry up?" Allan whispered in anguish, "We're going to be here all night!"

"Allan, how about you doing the clues?" Mrs Anderson suggested.

"Yes, fine, OK," he agreed, without any hesitation.

Mind you by that time he'd have agreed to anything in his anxiety to end the meeting and get away from them.

"Don't be so impatient with people," I said afterwards as I drove him over to the garage. "This treasure hunt sounds like it might be fun."

"Well, at least it couldn't be worse than those awful trips. You weren't here last year, but the whole thing — Oh, you turn right now," he directed.

"I know." I halted at the junction and waited for a break in the traffic.

"OK this side. On you go."

"There's a van coming."

"Where?" Allan made a great show of screwing up his eyes and peering out into the faraway distance.

"I'm not taking any risks, Allan."

"You could have been across and back again twice," he muttered irritably, drumming his fingers on the dashboard. "Right — now!"

"Allan, just sit back and stop fussing," I told him as I negotiated the junction. "You've got fifteen minutes before they close."

Men! Separate them from their precious cars for two seconds and they act like they've lost the Crown Jewels.

"Anyway, you're just in a bad mood because you hate being a passenger," I added just for good measure.

"Nothing of the kind," he retorted. "I don't mind that at all — if I feel reasonably confident about the driver."

"Meaning?" I took my eyes from the road for a second and glared at him.

THE CLUE TO HAPPINESS

"Meaning, that just as many accidents are caused by over-cautious drivers as —"

"Over-cautious! At least I don't fancy myself as the next Damon Hill! You drive as if —"

"Don't get all steamed up. I'm only saying —"

He broke off and yelled in annoyance. "Look, you've overshot the turn-off!"

He leapt up and down on the seat, looking for all the world like an overgrown infant in a baby-bouncer.

"We'll never make it now! Honestly, Lesley, you've worked in Shelby for a year now. You'd think you'd know your way about by this time."

"It's just as well we can't go in for the treasure hunt. With you navigating we'd end up in Spaghetti Junction!"

That did it. In the 10 months Allan and I have been going out, I've overlooked his occasional bursts of sarcasm. After all, you've got to make allowances, and when he's not obsessed about his silly old car, he can really be quite sweet.

But this time he had gone too far. Shouting at me like that when I was trying to do him a favour!

"Who says I'm not entering for the treasure hunt? Just because you're making up the clues doesn't mean to say I can't take part."

"Ha! That should be worth seeing! You couldn't find your way out of a one-way street without me to direct you. You'd be . . .

"Why are we stopping here?" he demanded.

I turned and regarded him icily.

"Because if you don't trust yourself in my hands, perhaps you'd feel happier in theirs!" I pointed to the bus stop along the road and checked my watch, slowly and carefully.

"There should be a bus that passes the garage in about twenty minutes."

The expression on his face was a delight to behold.

YOU can't," Pat Dunn said cheerfully when I went along to put my name down for the treasure hunt. "You'll need a navigator and everyone else is teamed up."

I frowned, uncomfortably aware of Allan sitting superciliously at her side.

"Never mind, Lesley," he said consolingly. "Why don't you just help Pat, Joan and me on the committee?"

He flashed me a forgive-and-forget smile, and I smiled back with all the sweetness I could muster.

"Thank you, but no," I said. "Actually I have got a partner."

Allan's smile faded.

"Who?" he asked.

"Just a friend." I replied. "He's not a club member, but there's no rule about that."

"No-o, but —"

"Well, then." I laid my £2 on the table. "See you next Saturday."

To say I had a partner lined up wasn't exactly true, but I couldn't let Allan think he was the only man in Shelby I'd more than a nodding acquaintance with.

And, anyway, there were five days to go till the hunt. Surely I could find someone in that time?

"Yes, of course you will dear," old Mrs Matthews from downstairs assured me when I told her of my predicament. She was putting out her milk bottle as I went up the stairs and she invited me in for a cup of tea.

"It's just that — well, I don't really know anyone here, except the others in the club," I went on doubtfully. "And most people tend to be busy on Saturdays anyway."

"This Saturday?" Mrs Matthews brightened up. "Then I've got the very answer! My nephew's son is coming through to spend the weekend with me. They used to live in Shelby, but they moved down to Leeds eighteen months ago.

"I'm sure he'd be delighted to go with you. In fact, it would solve a problem for me, too. I can't think what to do to entertain him over the weekend."

She nodded to a photograph on the mantelpiece. "That's Deryck there. I'll just go and phone, check that it's all right."

I had a surreptitious peek at the photograph while she was out in the hall. Staring back at me was one of the most handsome men I had ever seen.

"Yes, that's it fixed," Mrs Matthews said when she came back in. "He says he's very good at that sort of thing and he'd be delighted to help."

SUCCESS

What in life is termed "success"?
Position, wealth and gold,
The right to tell men what to do,
The power to have and hold?

The status symbols of the rich,
The thrills of world acclaim,
The stresses and the tensions
On the road that leads to fame?

Or is it in the byways,
The quiet walks of life,
We find our own fulfilment,
Away from fear and strife?

To rise up each and every day,
Content to do our best,
To live each moment as it comes,
To follow close our quest.

To make the most of what we have,
To envy not our fellows,
To live each season as it comes —
As life goes on and mellows.

To make the house wherein we live
A place of sweet content,
To welcome those who come and go,
Where joyful hours are spent.

And when our day is closing,
At the setting of our sun,
We'll lay aside our tools of life
And God will say, "Well done".

— Mrs E. B. Berry, Essex.

THE CLUE TO HAPPINESS

That would teach Allan, I thought during the remainder of the week. I could just picture his face when I turned up with the devastating Deryck! And to add insult to injury, I'd make sure we won their silly old treasure hunt, too. Judging from his photograph, Deryck looked the type who could do absolutely anything he set his mind to, and I couldn't wait to see him.

THERE you are, dear. He's ready and waiting," Mrs Matthews beamed at me when I went to her door on Saturday. "In you come. This is William."

"William?" I gazed in ill-disguised horror at the small bespectacled boy who stood with outstretched hand. "But I thought you said — I mean, wasn't it your nephew's son, Deryck —"

I tailed off, my eyes going to the picture on the mantelpiece.

"No, no. That's Deryck, my nephew," Mrs Matthews said proudly. "This is his son, William. Say hello, William."

"How do you do, Miss Brown?" William said brusquely. "Now, let's get down to business. I take it we'll go halves on the prize money?"

Whatever else could be said of William, he certainly didn't believe in wasting time.

"Er — well — yes," I started. "But I thought — I mean, that is . . ."

"After your petrol expenses have been deducted, of course," he went on seriously. "Right then — shall we get started?"

Oh, the embarrassment of it!

Give them their due, no-one at the club actually said anything when I arrived with 13-year-old Boy Wonder, but they didn't have to. The looks on their faces sufficed.

"I'll give out the first clue in a moment," Allan said from the centre of the hall, "but you mustn't open it till the signal.

"After that, it's everyone for himself, and we meet back here at seven for — er —" he looked pointedly at William "— drinks and dancing."

"Thank you," I said coolly as he handed us a small white envelope. Then, when everyone had received their clue we all scrambled out.

"What does it say?" I asked my partner as I started the car.

He took out the slip of paper and read aloud.

Rest has come for Mary Grieve
In 1910 she took her leave
But Mary left her last bequest
That other folk could also rest.

"Victoria Park," he went on. "Must be."

"Er, why must it be?" I asked patiently.

"Because that's where you're most likely to find benches, isn't it?" he replied, equally patiently.

"William, what's it got to do with benches? I don't understand."

He shot me a withering look.

"But it's obvious. It's one of those memorial benches people leave money for in their wills. All we've got to do is find one donated by Mary

Grieve. The obvious place to start looking is the park, isn't it?"

He regarded me owlishly from behind his spectacles.

"Yes, I suppose you're right."

There was no "suppose" about it. Of course William was right. William is the kind of child who is invariably right.

The fourth bench we checked bore a little brass plaque with the name and date, and I watched as he reached underneath to untape another of the familiar white envelopes.

I'd never noticed the plaque on that particular bench before, yet I'd sat on it many times last summer. It was the one overlooking the pond, where Allan and I used to sit and talk when we came to feed the ducks.

"We'll have to copy it down and replace the clue for the next person," William interrupted my thoughts. "Got a pen?"

I gave him one and he wrote it out, reading aloud as he did so.

Take the Longford road and try
To find a bird that doesn't fly.
Within you'll find a work of art
Which studied close will be your start.

"Right, genius, what do you make of that one?" I asked, when we went back to the car and headed out of town on the Longford road.

He was silent for a moment, studying it.

"What kind of birds don't fly?" he said musingly after a while.

"Ostriches?" I ventured.

William didn't deign to reply.

"Birds that don't fly," he repeated instead. "There must be some kind of catch to that. Just keep driving and let me think."

I was about to suggest nestlings, but at William's look I shut up, and when we came to the Crow Hotel I was glad I hadn't disgraced myself further.

"I don't know who made up these clues, but I don't think much of him," William said 15 minutes later. "They're so easy!"

We were heading for the disused watermill out at Locksley, the work of art in the last clue having been a picture of the old mill hanging in the hotel foyer.

I had noticed it before when Allan and I had dinner there to celebrate my birthday, and it had prompted a visit to the mill the following weekend.

That had been a nice day. We'd taken a picnic, and lain on the grass in the summer sunshine, talking about a million different things.

But the place looked different this time. Rain had started falling, and it seemed grey, depressing and gloomy.

"There it is," I said, as I spied the now familiar white envelope taped to a spar of the giant wheel.

Together we read the clue:

The wheels of time are turning round,
In prior days this place was found
Beside the road to Goltham Woods,

THE CLUE TO HAPPINESS

Where you might hope it still remains.

"Looks like he's run out of rhymes," I said, feeling suddenly unaccountably sorry for Allan's failure.

But William shook his head.

"No, I don't think so. There must be some reason for that. It has to be part of the clue."

He sat staring at it for 10 minutes, until I thought that he'd finally been stumped. Then he smiled in an infuriatingly superior manner.

"Oh, that's really quite clever!" he admitted. "Not bad at all."

"You've got it, then?" I asked.

"Of course!" He looked appalled that I could have doubted him. "Look — think it out for yourself. The key words are prior days, remains, and found — and, of course, the fact that there's no rhyme for woods."

I stared blankly at him.

"Well, what else would rhyme with woods?" he asked me.

"Moods?" I suggested cautiously. "Foods? Prudes? Goods?"

William gave an exasperated sigh.

"Jude's," he said. "The remains of St Jude's priory, on the outskirts of town at Goltham Woods. It was founded in prior times. Do you get it?"

"Oh," I said as light dawned.

B Y the time we got over to St Jude's, I was beginning to hope we wouldn't win the hunt. William was insufferable enough as it was! However, the only other club car we had seen was heading in the wrong direction, so it looked like we had a good chance of pulling it off.

The fifth clue was tacked into the crumbling masonry of the old priory, and William pulled it down and read aloud:

Beneath the branches of this tree,
The one that aye was dear to me
You'll see a spot with fresh turned soil.
Which spells the end of all your toil.

William frowned in perplexity.

"But there's millions of trees about here!" he exclaimed. "How on earth are we supposed to find the right one?"

It was my turn to smile.

"It's that one over there," I said pointing. "It's obvious, isn't it?"

William stared at me, and I enjoyed my little moment of triumph before quoting:

" 'Oh rowan tree, oh, rowan tree, thou'll aye be dear to me.' Is that song a bit before your time, sonny?"

He glowered briefly before marching over to the one and only rowan tree in sight. It was a huge one, with thick luxuriant foliage and a mass of red berries.

"There's the fresh-turned soil, anyway," he said. "Got anything to dig with?"

I hadn't, but he produced a penknife and managed to scrape away enough earth to reveal a small box wrapped in a plastic bag. I took it out, and unfolded the piece of paper that accompanied it and read:

Within this little box you'll find
A token of my heart and mind
And if you will accept, I'll strive
To keep my mouth shut when you drive.

"It's supposed to be money!" William yelled indignantly as I opened the box.

"Belt up!" I told him, staring in wonder at the diamond which glinted back at me. "Just belt up, William."

"I will not!" he went on. "You got me here on the understanding that we'd half twenty quid. Instead it's a rotten old glass ring!"

"Cheeky little whelp!" a voice issued from the foliage above. "Glass indeed! I'll have you know it's a diamond, and I could have put a deposit down on a new sports car with what it cost!"

"Oh, Allan!" I gazed ruefully at him as he slithered down. "That's the most — beautiful, romantic, wonderful thing I've ever heard of!"

He grunted, and extracted a twig from his collar.

"Yes, well, maybe so. But after two hours stuck up there, I'm not feeling particularly romantic now. So are you going to marry me or not?"

"Yes!" I said delightedly. I threw my arms around his neck, and the disgruntled expression softened.

"What about the others?" I asked him.

"Oh, they should just about have reached clue number five on the real treasure hunt," he said. "That one's much longer than yours was. It should take till at least seven o'clock. Which means —" he added brightly "— that we can forget about them for nearly three hours."

"Yes, but you can't forget about me," William piped up irately, reminding me of his presence. "You got me here under false pretences. I won the treasure hunt, so I want my half of the money. That's ten pounds."

He stuck out his hand and his lower lip simultaneously.

"But you wouldn't necessarily have won if you'd been on the real hunt," Allan pointed out. "I'll give you fifty pence and we'll call it quits."

"Five pounds," William demanded menacingly.

"Two pounds." Allan upped his offer.

"Five!"

"Three."

"Five!"

"You're not on," Allan started. "If you think I'm —"

"Five, and I'll get the bus back to town," William threw in craftily.

I suppose Allan must have given in, because when I looked up William was already stepping it out in the direction of the bus stop.

"You can drive back to town," I said sweetly, handing Allan my car keys.

"No, no. You drive," he insisted. "I don't mind."

"Really, I'd much rather you drove," I said, as we returned to the car.

"Tell you what," he suggested. "Let's toss for it!" □

A Valuable Lesson

I SAW a big brown hare in the lochside field today. He sat up and struck both his forepaws together which immediately reminded me of my old school headmaster, Dr Hare.

He was a tall, spare figure, immaculate in morning dress, who moved with military precision.

A strict disciplinarian, he never used the "corrective" instruments that lay in his cupboard, like the bamboo cane and leather tawse, and seemed to rely solely on the aura that surrounded him, with his slicked-back silver hair and neatly-clipped moustache to match. He had real "Presence".

Dr Hare had only to raise one silver-plated eyebrow to bring a complete blanket of silence down on a chattering class and make any scholar shake in his, or her, shoes.

His chief delight was to take the natural history period, leaving us in no doubt that his knowledge regarding the flora and fauna of Scotland was second to none.

He also organised a nature afternoon, out of doors, on the Pentland Hills. This was an entirely new experience for us and we dutifully followed Dr Hare, each clutching a small chart with pictures of birds, beasts and insects we were likely to see, together with painted posies of wild flowers and plants to study carefully and avoid treading underfoot.

Nothing was named so we had to find out for ourselves what we had seen and try to match our discoveries with the illustrations on the chart.

GIDEON'S WAY

More impressions of life from the Highlands of Scotland, by Gideon Scott May, observer of people and nature alike...

It also had a column on the extreme right depicting different sets of footprints. Some were boldly stamped, others barely discernible, but all were descriptively different signatures in sand, earth or snow, from which we were required to decipher, and correctly name, the bird or beast which had left their footmarks behind.

This was a part of schooling I learned to love and it left me with something to treasure — an early insight into Nature's wonderful world.

That afternoon I had crept silently through the undergrowth, always ahead of my classmates, because they talked too much and had no chance of catching the wild creatures unawares, like the fox I found fast asleep.

What a moment to remember when he suddenly woke up and we found ourselves face to face, but not for more than a split second, as the fox bounded out of his bed in the bracken and vanished with a wave of his russet-red brush.

Dr Hare always finished the afternoon's outing by asking, "Does anyone know the difference between a stoat and a weasel?"

Those of us who had heard the well-worn question before groaned inwardly, but dutifully shook our heads and the doctor, delighted that nobody knew, explained that the "weasel was weasely distinguished, while the stoat was stoatally different!"

A STOAT spent the worst part of last winter sleeping snugly in a bag of sheepswool that hung in a wooden shed next to the house. Irralee saw him first one morning when he stuck his head out of the wool sack.

He was "stoatally" different all right, being pure white with beady black eyes. He was dressed in his winter coat, or ermine, used traditionally to trim the robes of royalty, which didn't seem to worry our stoat, tucked up in the

Gideon is horrified when he discovers the fate of the precious hens' eggs, but he insists that the culprit get a hot meal before leaving Croft Douglas . . .

warm security of the wool sack.

He left sometime in the spring and the next time I saw him he was wearing his brown and cream summer coat, and disappeared with a flash of his black-tipped tail into the henhouse, only to reappear, seconds later, bowling a big brown egg in front of him with the clever dexterity of a World Cup footballer.

So this is the explanation for the hens' poor performance! Even the china eggs had vanished and I found them in various places where the stoat had tried, in vain, to break them against a stone.

All this was a little more than worrying as our special Maran hens systematically search the fields and woods for food — beechmast, hazelnuts, acorns and the green grass which they graze constantly to colour the yolk of their eggs and supply us with dark brown containers crammed with natural goodness that these busy, bustling, speckled hens have travelled far and wide to gather from the countryside.

Whenever I have a problem I give it some serious thought before going to sleep and, sure enough, I usually wake in the morning with a solution.

AN early visit to the henhouse rewards me with a newly-laid egg, still warm in the nest. At least I had beaten the brown bandit to this one.

Carefully, I drilled a hole in each end and blew out half the contents of the egg, replacing them by pouring in a generous spoonful of curry powder.

I then sealed each end with Sellotape, shook the egg vigorously to ensure that this would be the warmest of cocktails, then placed it prominently in a nest facing the henhouse door.

In two hours' time the egg had gone and afterwards the hens seemed much happier. By midday their nests were once more full of eggs.

I saw the stoat tonight in the lochside woods. He popped out suddenly from behind a silver birch tree to sit up and survey me for a second as if he wanted to say something.

I knew exactly what it was — a more than meaningful comment about "curried eggs!" ■

Illustration by Michelle Ross.

47

YOUR VERSES

AN APOLOGY

"I'm sorry" — such a simple phrase
And yet it means so much.
To one who's hurt and smarting
It's like a healing touch.
The power in those little words
A broken heart can mend,
And when we're truly sorry
We find that we can send
Our loving thoughts to heal the wound
To comfort and uplift,
And once we are forgiven
We find we've bridged the rift,
For when we say those special words
That heal, bless and restore,
The barriers come tumbling down
And we are friends once more.

K.G., Twickenham.

MY BEST FRIEND

When I was a baby my friends were my elders,
Especially my mum and my dad.
Then, aged four, sadly I lost him —
My dad, the best friend I had.

My mother soon tried to take over.
She tried, but she wasn't to blame
When the shoulder she gave me to cry on
Somehow just wasn't the same.

So I turned to my brothers and sisters.
There were seven in all — young and old.
They too offered shoulders to cry on,
And a piece of their hearts — made of gold.

But I knew no-one could replace him.
And the pain in my heart made me sad.
Though decades have passed, I still miss him,
My dad — the best friend I had.

Mr F. C., Hornchurch.

48

ROSES IN HEAVEN

There's roses in Heaven for you and for me,
We continue what's started on earth you see,
For if love is pure, and love is true,
Your meeting together comes in view,
As soon as you step through the heavenly door,
Your loved one is waiting for ever more.

There's roses in Heaven, for you and for me,
As you approach the door, with a Heavenly key
And a wonderful sight awaits us there,
Loved ones waiting and as they stare,
They're as real to you, as they used to be,
Enfolding their arms around you and me.

There's roses in Heaven, for you and for me,
It's all God's plan above you see,
And as we depart once more to earth,
We continue the plan of life and birth,
So this pattern of travel goes on until,
The world and the Heavens all stand still.

P.G., Leicester.

YOUR WORLD

Bluebells nod in a gentle breeze,
Anemones shine likes stars,
A nightingale sings way up in the trees,
And all of this is ours.

Wavelets rustling the shingle shore,
Echo the gull's mournful cry,
All this is life, all this and more,
It belongs to you and I.

If chimneys and rooftops are your view,
And traffic noise fills the air,
Wherever you are, whatever you do,
There's a beautiful world out there.

Mrs T.A., Harwich.

Complete
Story
by
ISOBEL
STEWART

Once upon a time, many years ago, a girl refused to marry anyone but the man she loved. And because of her, a girl of today learned to live happily ever after.

An Old-Fashioned Love Story

THERE can't be very many grandmothers like mine. She didn't ask me any questions, she didn't offer me any advice. She did tell me, as always, that I was too thin, and wondered if I was still drinking black coffee on an empty stomach. But after that, she waited.

AN OLD-FASHIONED LOVE STORY

We went for a walk. I helped her to pick out some weeds in the garden, and watched while she made a batch of scones.

Then she tried once again to get me interested in pottery. She got so involved in the ceramic pig she was making, that she left me to make lunch, and when we had finished she got out the brasses, and we polished them together.

It began to rain heavily so we lit the fire. As we polished the brasses I had known and loved since I was small, and saw the firelight reflected in them, I knew that now I could talk.

"Gran," I said slowly.

She put down the ornament which she was polishing.

"All right, Kate," she said, quietly. "I've heard your mother's side of it. Do you want to tell me yours?"

I could feel a defensive knot forming inside me.

"What did she tell you?" I asked, unable to keep the hostility out of my voice.

But Gran ignored it.

"I'm sure you could guess," she replied. "She said that she was sending you to me for a holiday, because you had been overworking. She hoped I could persuade you to stay for the fortnight and keep you relaxed."

"That's not all she said," I told her flatly.

"No, it isn't," she agreed. "She also told me that they were very worried because you were determined to marry an unsuitable man. They had managed to persuade you to reconsider, and she hoped I would do the same."

I didn't want to cry, but the tears were there, and it wasn't easy to speak.

"Did she tell you why they won't accept him?" I asked, shakily, and went on without giving her a chance to answer — "Because he's ten years older than I am, and he's a widower with two children, and he's an overworked and underpaid teacher."

My grandmother nodded. "Yes, she did tell me all that," she said, calmly. "But there must be more to it, Kate."

The firelight gleamed on the polished brass, and my eyes blurred.

"Oh yes," I told her, and now my voice was steady. "There's much, much more. David is — well, he's my man, that's all, Gran. He's quiet, kind, and thoughtful. We laugh at the same things and I've never, in all my life, known anyone I could talk to as easily as I can talk to him."

She waited, as I paused.

"And I love him," I said positively. "I can't imagine not spending the rest of my life with him."

"That's what I wanted to hear," Gran said, with satisfaction. And then, before I could relax, she went on: "But I'm sure you can see why your mother and father want you to be quite certain. After all, it won't be easy starting off married life with two children. Or will it?"

"No," I admitted. "It won't be easy."

I told her about David's children. Rebecca was nine, a thin, dark, intense child, and you could see that David was the centre of her world. She was fiercely possessive of him, and when we were all together she was hostile and withdrawn.

No, Rebecca would not easily accept me as a stepmother. She had David's smoky-grey eyes, and his determined chin, and sometimes, when she wasn't being difficult on purpose, there was something so young and so vulnerable about her, that I ached to put my arms around her. But I knew it would be a long, long time before she would let me do that.

STEVIE was different. Two years younger, fair-haired, blue eyes. David had said that he was like his mother in many ways, being easy-going and sunny-natured, taking each day as it came.

But over the five years since Mary had died, Stevie had found that a few tears, a trembling lip, and an impulsive hug, could smooth out most of his problems, allowing him to do pretty much what he wanted to.

A succession of housekeepers had taken him into their hearts, and spoilt him more and more.

Now — and David knew it — Stevie was in danger of becoming a self-centred little boy who relied on his charm to get him out of anything.

I could love Stevie, and I was pretty sure I could love Rebecca, if they would give me a chance. But I had to be honest and realistic, and when Gran asked me, I had to admit that it would be hard going, for all of us.

"At least," she said, when I had finished, "you haven't got a sentimental picture of yourself becoming an instant mother for them."

I looked down at my hands, ringless because my parents had asked me to wait and think things over before giving David my promise to marry him, and accepting the small garnet he had bought for me.

"I didn't, even at the start," I told her honestly, "but they were part of David's life, and I knew that if I couldn't cope with them, there was no point in going on."

Gran got up and switched the kettle on.

"And you feel you can cope?" she asked me.

"Yes," I said quietly. "It won't be easy, but I'll do it."

The treacherous tears were very near. "But I wish I could make Mum and Dad see that. Oh, Gran, David and I love each other, and — we'll be all right, because of that. They find it difficult to see that."

Gran made the tea and brought it over to the fire.

"I wonder," she said thoughtfully, "if you know the story of Great-Aunt Helen?"

"Great-Aunt Helen?"

"No," Gran said, "I don't suppose you've even heard of her, but your mum and dad have. Still, I don't suppose going over a long story like that would make it any easier for them to accept you marrying David."

Suddenly I was curious.

"Tell me about her, Gran."

Continued on page 54.

A Place

Take a pretty piece of material, edge it with this knitted lace and you have an elegant centrepiece to grace any table.

Materials Required – Of **Coats Anchor Mercer-Crochet Cotton No. 20** 2 x 10 gram balls selected colour; set of four 2¾ mm (No. 12) Milward knitting needles with points at both ends (if your knitting is loose, use a size finer needle; if tight, use a size larger needle); Milward steel crochet hook 1.25 (No. 3); piece of fabric 25 cm, *9¾ inches*, in diameter; toning sewing thread; Coats bias binding (optional).

For best results it is essential to use the recommended yarn. If you have difficulty in obtaining the yarn, write direct, enclosing a stamped, addressed envelope, to the following address for stockists: Consumer Services Department, Coats Crafts UK, McMullen Road, Darlington, Co. Durham DL1 1YQ. Tel: 01325 365457.

Tension – 8 sts. and 11 rows to 2.5-cm, square over stocking-stitch.

Measurement – Depth of edging – 9.5 cm. Finished size – 42 cm, in diameter.

Abbreviations – **K** – knit; **P** – purl; **st.(s)** – stitch(es); **sl.** – slip; **tog.** – together; **p.s.s.o.** – pass slipped stitch over; **y.fwd.** – yarn forward; **y.r.n.** – yarn round needle; **M2 (make 2)** – into next stitch work K1 P1 and K1; **t.b.l.** – through back of loop; **d.c.** – double crochet; **ch.** – chain; **s.s.** – slip stitch.

For Lace

Cast on 204 sts., 68 on each of 3 needles. Knit 3 rounds.

4th round – *Sl.1, K2 tog., p.s.s.o., y.fwd., K2 tog., y.fwd., K10, y.fwd., sl.1, K1, p.s.s.o., y.fwd.; repeat from * to end.

5th round – Knit.

6th round – *K1, K2 tog., y.fwd., K4, K2 tog., y.r.n. twice, sl.1., K1, p.s.s.o., K4, y.fwd., sl.1., K1, p.s.s.o.; repeat from * to end.

7th and alternate rounds – Knit, working K1 and P1 into each "y.r.n. twice" of previous round.

8th round – Before commencing round, knit first 2 sts. from left-hand needle on to right-hand needle, mark beginning of round with a coloured thread, *y.fwd., K4, K2 tog., (M2) twice, sl.1, K1, p.s.s.o., K4, y.fwd., sl.1, K2 tog., p.s.s.o.; repeat from * to end. [228 sts.]

10th round – *K4, K2 tog., K1 t.b.l., P1, K1 t.b.l., y.r.n. twice, K1 t.b.l., P1, K1 t.b.l., sl.1, K1, p.s.s.o., K3, K2 tog., y.fwd.; repeat from * to end.

11th and alternate rounds – As 7th round working knit t.b.l. into t.b.l. sts. of previous round and purl into purl sts. of previous round.

12th round – *K3, K2 tog., K1 t.b.l., P1, K1 t.b.l., (M2) twice, K1 t.b.l., P1, K1 t.b.l., sl.1, K1, p.s.s.o., K4; repeat from * to end. [252 sts.]

14th round – *K2, K2 tog., (K1 t.b.l., P1, K1 t.b.l.) twice, y.r.n. twice, (K1 t.b.l., P1, K1 t.b.l.) twice, sl.1, K1, p.s.s.o., K3; repeat from * to end.

16th round – *K1, K2 tog., (K1 t.b.l., P1, K1 t.b.l.) twice, (M2) twice, (K1 t.b.l., P1, K1 t.b.l.) twice, sl.1, K1, p.s.s.o., K2; repeat from * to end. [276 sts.]

18th round – *K2 tog., (K1 t.b.l., P1, K1 t.b.l.) 3 times, y.r.n. twice, (K1 t.b.l., P1, K1 t.b.l.) 3 times, sl.1, K1, p.s.s.o., K1; repeat from * to end.

20th round – Before commencing round, knit first st. of left-hand needle on to right-hand needle, *(K1 t.b.l., P1, K1 t.b.l.) 3 times, (M2) twice, (K1 t.b.l., P1, K1 t.b.l.) 3 times, sl.1, K2 tog., p.s.s.o.; repeat from * to end. [300 sts.]

22nd round – *(K1 t.b.l., P1, K1 t.b.l.) 4 times, y.fwd., (K1 t.b.l., P1, K1 t.b.l.) 4 times, y.fwd., K1 t.b.l., y.fwd.; repeat from * to end. [336 sts.]

24th round – *(K1 t.b.l., P1, K1 t.b.l.) 4 times, M2, (K1 t.b.l., P1, K1 t.b.l.) 4 times, y.fwd., sl.1, K2 tog., p.s.s.o., y.fwd.; repeat from * to end. [360 sts.]

26th, 28th and 30th rounds – *(K1 t.b.l., P1, K1 t.b.l.) 9 times, y.fwd., sl.1, K2 tog., p.s.s.o., y.fwd.; repeat from * to end.

32nd round – Work sts. as set. [360 sts.]

OUTER EDGING

Using crochet hook, work *1 d.c. into next 3 sts. and slip off needle, 10 ch.; repeat from *, ending with 1 s.s. into first d.c.

Fasten off.

INNER EDGING

With right side facing attach thread to cast-on edge and work a row of d.c. evenly round cast-on edge, ending with 1 s.s. into first d.c.

Fasten off.

Damp and pin out to measurements.

TO MAKE UP

Turn back a small hem on fabric or face with bias binding. Place edging to fabric and sew neatly in position. ■

AN OLD-FASHIONED LOVE STORY

Continued from page 51.

She smiled and nodded. "I only know her story second-hand. My grandmother, who was her sister, told it to me, when I was a little girl."

"So she was your Great-Aunt Helen?" I asked. "That's a long time ago."

"Yes," Gran agreed. "But somehow, I think you and Helen might have a lot in common." And she told Helen's story.

HELEN ELIZABETH BROWNE was the youngest of the four Browne girls — and the prettiest. But none of her sisters could ever feel jealous, because Helen was loved by everyone. She was sweet, kind, gentle, helpful and obedient. She played the piano, and sang a little — she did embroidery, just a little.

Her special interest at home was the garden. She loved to be surrounded by flowers, and somehow they seemed to grow better for Helen than for anyone else.

Helen, everyone agreed, would make a good marriage. Her two eldest sisters were married, and her next sister engaged, all to suitable men, but no-one doubted that Helen would do much better.

And so it was no surprise when Lord Clevely's youngest son, home from the Army, began to be a regular caller at the Browne house. Soon Helen was invited to play croquet and have tea at the manor.

Helen's parents agreed that it was the right match for her. Mrs Browne began to make plans for the wedding.

All that remained was for Rupert to propose, and make it official.

Mrs Browne was quite certain that all Rupert lacked was the opportunity. She thought he was possibly lacking in initiative, but she forgave him because he was a pleasant and well-mannered young man. In order to help things along, she began to arrange situations where Rupert and Helen could be alone.

One afternoon, knowing that Rupert would be calling, she sent Helen into the garden to gather some flowers. Helen was looking very pretty that day, in her white muslin dress, surrounded by the bright colours of the flowers.

No man could resist her, Mrs Browne thought, with satisfaction.

Helen went gladly into the garden, and was so absorbed with her flowers, that when a voice greeted her, she swung round, surprised.

A young man, whom she had never seen before, stood there. He was extremely untidy, with wavy, dark hair, and unpressed trousers, but his smile was wide and friendly.

"You look marvellous!" he told her enthusiastically. "I wish I could paint you, just like that."

"Are you an artist?" Helen asked.

He shook his head. "I can't draw a recognisable cat," he said cheerfully. "But I wish I was an artist, so that I could paint your portrait."

Somehow he had come close to her now, and smiling, he took her basket from her.

54

AN OLD-FASHIONED LOVE STORY

"I'll carry this for you," he said, taking in the beauty of the garden. "You can't imagine what it means to me, to be in a garden like this."

"Why?" Helen asked him, without thinking that she didn't even know him.

"I've been in Africa," he told her. "I'm a doctor at a mission hospital out in the middle of nowhere and haven't seen a garden like this for years!" He smiled down at her. "Or a girl like you. You must be Miss Helen Browne, I suppose."

Bewildered, Helen agreed that was her name.

"I'm Christopher Wilson." He smiled. "My aunt is Miss Wilson in Bradfield Crescent. She sent me along with a note to your mother, but when I saw you, I just had to speak to you."

Helen had never met anyone like this large, enthusiastic young man before.

They sat on the garden bench and he told her about his work in the mission station. He told her of the months with no rain.

He spoke about the patients, who were slowly beginning to trust him and believe that the white doctor really did know how to make people better. He described the long journeys he made to visit people too far away to come to the mission hospital, and he told her of the gradual breaking-down of the old superstitions, and the slow acceptance of the church which had sent him there.

"It's a dreadful place," he told her, cheerfully, looking around at her garden, "bleak and bare. I'll think of this, when I go back."

Helen's heart gave a most peculiar bump.

"When are you going back?" she asked him.

"In a month," he told her. "They need me there, Miss Helen. There isn't any doctor there just now, so I've got to get back."

He pulled his watch out of his pocket abruptly, and looked at it. "Oh no," he said, "I'm supposed to be at the station right now, to meet the Reverend Mr Clark. He's coming for my report on my progress. Goodbye, Miss Helen — I'll come and see you again."

Then he was gone, having forgotten, Helen realised, the note he was supposed to give her mother.

She sat there on the garden bench, feeling a little dazed, with Christopher's image so clear in her mind, that later on when Rupert Clevely came down the path, it took her a minute to realise who he was.

WELL, Helen?" her mother prompted at dinner that night, with an encouraging smile. "What do you mean, Mamma?" "I mean that Rupert was with you for rather a long time, this afternoon."

"Yes, he was," she quietly agreed, looking away.

Her mother and father waited, but Helen said nothing more.

Finally, Mrs Browne could contain herself no longer.

"Well, Helen?" she asked, impatiently. "Did he ask you to marry him?"

AN OLD-FASHIONED LOVE STORY

Helen was silent, but warm colour crept into her cheeks.

"It's all right," her father said. "I know you're concerned because he approached you before talking to me, but — well, things are changing with young folk, and I don't hold it against him. I'm sure he'll be coming round to see me."

Helen's brown eyes met her father's.

"No, Papa," she said clearly.

"What do you mean?" her mother demanded. "Do you mean no, Rupert will not be coming, or — or no, he did not ask you?"

Helen sighed and said, "Yes, he did ask me, Mamma, but he will not be coming to see Papa, because I said I couldn't marry him."

There was a long silence in the dining-room. Mr Browne's face slowly became redder and redder, while Helen's became paler and paler. But she did not look away.

"Why, may I ask, do you find that you cannot marry Lord Clevely's younger son?" Mr Browne asked, at last.

"Because I do not love him, Papa," she said, calmly and simply.

Her mother laughed in relief.

"My dear, romantic child," she said, fondly. "There is no need to worry about that. Marry Rupert, and love will grow in time. Now, if that is all —"

"I cannot marry Rupert," Helen repeated. "He is not the sort of man I could love."

This was the first time Helen had been stubborn in all her eighteen years. Her parents looked helplessly at each other, and Mrs Browne sighed deeply. "Leave her," she said gently. "She'll come to her senses."

As Mr Browne rose from the table, he said, "I suppose you're entitled to keep him on a string for a bit, Helen, but take care."

Helen was silent.

TIGER OF THE NIGHT

Faintly stirring, eyes so bright,
Little tiger of the night.
A sigh, a yawn, a tongue so pink,
Curls, and then those bright eyes blink.

Stretch those legs, flex those claws,
Little tiger, the night is yours.
Yellow stripes in the moonlight shine,
The night is yours, but you are mine.

Stalking, hunting, keeping low,
You've spotted something, that I know.
With a wiggle of your tail and a mighty roar,
You leap twelve inches off the floor.

Early the next morning, Christopher Wilson came to call on Helen again.

Mrs Browne was busy with the cook, and the maid showed Christopher into the drawing-room, and then called Helen for him.

Helen came running down the stairs, her dark hair loose on her shoulders.

"Maybe I shouldn't have come so early," Christopher said, his eyes on her face.

"I'm glad you did," she told him, meaning every word she said.

Christopher sat down on the couch, and Helen sat beside him. They were talking, or rather, Christopher was talking eagerly about his new ideas that he was trying to introduce at his mission hospital, when the door opened and Mrs Browne came in.

"How do you do, Mrs Browne?" Christopher said, rising and holding out his hand.

"I have a note from my aunt, Miss Wilson, for you — should have given it to you yesterday, but I met Miss Helen in the garden, and everything else went out of my mind."

Well, that was understandable, Mrs Browne thought, for even a very unsuitable young man such as this must have feelings. No doubt when he returned to that dreadful place his aunt had told her about he would often think of Helen.

IT was only a week later that Christopher and Helen came to Mr and Mrs Browne, hand in hand, and said that they wished to be married.

"I'm sorry, Christopher," Mr Browne said, trying to hide his surprise, "but of course it is quite out of the question."

"Papa," Helen said quietly, "we love each other."

And come to land, your quarry snared,
Those bright eyes looking oddly scared.
What do I do now? you seem to wonder,
Those hunter instincts cast asunder.

It's only a leaf, little kitten cat,
Let it go, you can't kill that,
And come inside, back to the light,
My little tiger of the night.

— Mrs T. A., Essex.

57

AN OLD-FASHIONED LOVE STORY

"I can well believe that you two young people have — ah — an affection for each other," Mr Browne agreed, and with some difficulty, he smiled. "But marriage is not possible."

He spoke very pleasantly, and very reasonably. And so did Christopher.

"Why not, Mr Browne?" he asked.

"Well, now," said Mr Browne, "surely it would be hard for a young man of such vision to give up work which obviously means so much to him."

"Why should I give it up?" Christopher asked, surprised. "Helen will help me."

Beside him, Helen nodded vigorously.

Her father thought, fleetingly, that he had never, until this moment, noticed that Helen's chin had such a determined set to it.

"How can Helen live in a place like that?" he asked.

Helen's dark-brown eyes met his, steadily.

"I can live wherever Christopher lives," she said with certainty.

Mr Brown turned to Christopher and lowered his voice. "And what about when — I mean if — well, if you and Helen should —"

"Helen is a healthy young woman," Christopher said cheerfully. "She'll have her babies with no trouble at all."

Mrs Browne wondered, afterwards, why she hadn't fainted at the shock of it all.

"Edward," she murmured shakily, turning to her husband, "You can't allow it —"

"Of course not," Mr Browne assured her. "Christopher — Helen — I want to hear no more of this. It's out of the question, and I refuse to give my consent. I'm sorry, but the matter is closed."

"No, Papa," Helen said, clearly, and her father looked at her, astounded that she had contradicted him.

"We do wish to have your consent, but if you refuse to give it, that will not stop me marrying Christopher. We will run away. You will not stop us, so —"

For the first time, her voice shook. "So please, dear Papa, dear Mamma — be happy for us, and give us your blessing, because we do, truly, love each other."

"Love!" Mr Browne exclaimed in exasperation. "And will you please tell me, Helen, what you know about love in all the wisdom of your eighteen years?"

"Only this, Papa," she replied. "That it makes you brave enough — and strong enough — to face whatever comes." She paused, and added in a quiet voice: "And do things that you never thought you'd dare."

Two weeks later Christopher and Helen were married. Helen had steadily held to her unswerving determination to marry Christopher — and kept her courage in the face of her mother's tears and sulks, and her father's threats.

It wasn't easy for a girl so young, and so used to always doing what her parents told her to do, but then, what lay ahead would not be easy, either. Bit by bit her parents softened, and in the end they agreed.

IT was a simple wedding, much simpler than her other sisters' weddings had been. And when it was over, Mr Browne, blowing his nose once again, had to admit that he had never seen a more radiant bride or a more loving bridegroom.

"We'll never see Helen again." Mrs Browne wept as the carriage with the newly-married pair drove off towards the ship that would take them to Africa. "But oh, Edward — how wonderful, to love each other like that!"

Mr Browne watched until the carriage was out of sight.

"Yes, my dear," he agreed, and blew his nose again. "It is wonderful."

My grandmother sat looking into the firelight, and she was smiling.

"And did they?" I asked softly. "Did they ever see Helen again?"

"Oh yes," she said. "Helen and Christopher came back every few years. Clarissa — my grandmother — told me that Helen's fair skin was quite brown, but Helen didn't seem to mind. She never had fashionable dresses, because Christopher couldn't afford them, and in any case, there was no-one to see them at the mission hospital.

"They had three children, two boys and then a little girl. Oh, but they were happy, so very happy, Kate."

She smiled, remembering, and I smiled, too, more readily than I had done in weeks. I felt a bond with my unknown great-aunt, whose love had made her brave enough and strong enough to face whatever came. She and Christopher had loved each other, and because of that everything had been all right.

I stood up.

"Can I use the phone, Gran? I want to phone David to tell him that I'm coming home, and I'm going to tell Mum and Dad that I have done my thinking.

"I love David, and I'm going to marry him. I know it won't be easy, and I can understand that they are anxious, but — I know what I'm doing."

I think Dad knew right away why I was calling; he accepted my certainty. He didn't interrupt, and when I had finished, he was quiet for a moment.

"All right, love," he said at last. "Come home, bring David and — we'll talk about things. No, your mother's out, but — I'll tell her."

I said goodbye and passed the phone to Gran.

It would be all right, I thought. Once they accepted my decision, they would be with us all the way, they would give me all the help I needed — and help I would need. With Rebecca and Stevie.

I could hear Gran on the phone. I smiled as I heard her words. "Remember Great-Aunt Helen," she was telling my father.

Gran was a dear. As she put the receiver down she turned towards me, a warm smile lighting up her face. □

"GOODBYE,

BOTH THEIR WORKING LIVES WERE OVER. ALL THAT REMAINED WAS THIS, THEIR LAST DAY TOGETHER . . .

"OLD FELLER"

**Complete Story by
JOYCE STRANGER**

THE alarm clock woke Jake at 4 a.m. — for the last time. The last time. He sat up, forcing his stiff legs to obey his brain, and ran a gnarled hand through the thick, grey hair. Even now, at 72, he was proud of his fine head of hair.

The Jack Russel sat up and watched him, prick-eared. Dog knew the day's routine as well as his master did. Nell would never have allowed Dog in the bedroom. But Nell had been dead for almost ten years, and the animal was company in the silent room.

Jake held out his hand and Dog came to him, leaning for a moment against his master. That, too, was part of the day's routine.

The last time.

Jake looked round the room. Today everything would be packed away, to take out in another room, in another home. Not his home.

Outside the window he heard the familiar noises as Majesty moved in the straw. It was time to begin the day. He felt as young as ever in his mind, but his body refused to work at the speed he had once taken for granted. His fingers had once been so gentle with a horse . . .

"It's cold, Dog," Jake said, as the shiver in the air struck his body. Jake named his horses, but every dog he owned was Dog.

Dog trotted behind his

"GOODBYE, OLD FELLER"

master into the tiny, cold bathroom. Jake could not hurry, even though the floor was icy under his bare feet. He wanted to savour these last hours in the cottage where he had brought Nell when they married, over 50 years ago.

The Old Gaffer had been here then; the same age as Jake and more of a friend than a master, by the time he'd died.

Jake stared at his own face in the mirror. He looked at a skin not yet too wrinkled; at bright blue eyes that still held laughter; at the teeth that were still strong and white.

"No use feeling sorry for yourself," he said to his reflection, and Dog wagged his short tail in furious approval.

They went back to the bedroom, to the ritual of dressing. It took longer these days, as everything did.

Jake looked at the sampler that Nell's mother had made for them, long ago.

Grant me the serenity to accept what I cannot change; the courage to change what I can; and the wisdom to know the difference.

Today he needed serenity and courage. Today he would part with his horse. He and Majesty had been together since the day the old Shire was foaled. Jake had handled him two minutes after his birth; had gentled him and coaxed him and taught him to draw the big carts, to parade at the shows, to wear his regalia with pride.

"Lucky Dog," Jake said, as he finally pulled on his thick anorak. "You don't know that tomorrow will be different. Tomorrow we'll wake somewhere else, you and me. Not here."

Not here, a voice said relentlessly in his head, as he walked down the steep, narrow staircase and into the little morning-room.

Not here, the voice said, as he went into the kitchen and put out food for Dog.

Dog gobbled his meal as if he'd never been fed before, and Jake watched him affectionately. At least he wasn't losing Dog.

T HE day had begun outside the windows, in spite of the dark and the cold of morning. He could see the dew on the climbing honeysuckle outside the window. Dew reminded him of his boyhood, long ago, when his father had been horse-master on the farm.

His father had been dead too long, and now the last Shire was standing in the stable, on his last day on the farm. Majesty was being retired and Jake was being retired, but the farm would go on without a horse-master and without any horses at all.

It seemed like treason.

When the Old Gaffer died, it was his eldest daughter, Marian, and her husband, George, who took over the farm. Not that George made a bad Gaffer, but he had never been a man for horses.

Outside, voices called to one another and a man laughed. That laugh was Barney's — Barney who loved the cows as he loved nothing else.

Barney was old, too — but there was still a place for him, and they weren't pulling down his cottage to make room for the new motorway.

When Bob came home from Canada, with Jake's grandchildren, there would be nothing left to see. At least Rosie's children had had the benefit of knowing this place, of running through the door begging to see the big horses. How little Jakie loved the horses!

Jake smiled, thinking about his grandson. He had promised Jakie that the old brasses would hang by the mantelshelf in his mother's home. They would always be there, as a reminder . . . The big scrapbooks were ready, too.

There seemed so little of his life, away from horses.

The mantelpiece above the fireplace was bright with red rosettes, and covered with the tiny trophies the Gaffer had had made, copies of the big trophies they'd won.

Jake had been horse-master after his father. How he'd loved the life!

Gaffer George had been a young man then, and Jake had tried to teach him to love the horses. But that love was born, not made; and it wasn't there. The young Gaffer kept one or two horses for old times' sake, and perhaps for Jake's sake; but they had stopped breeding.

Majesty was Emperor's grandson.

Jake could remember Emperor so well — his black coat gleaming, the light in his eyes, the prancing trot. And Majesty was almost 30 now; his father had been Prince Hal, one of the last sons of the Emperor.

Jake finished his breakfast, thinking about Majesty.

"Work to do, Dog," he said, and at once Dog was by the door.

Jake closed the doors of the all-night stove, drew back the curtains, and switched off the light. The little voice inside him repeated over and over: the last time — you'll never do this again . . .

H E didn't want to think about tomorrow. About the empty stable that Majesty would never see again, or about the new bed he would wake in, with no need to get up early to go out to the old horse. "Time you rested," the Gaffer had said, with kindness in his voice. But Jake had looked at him, stony-eyed. Who wanted to sit waiting for the end, doing nothing?

"It is time, Dad," Rosie had said. She was very like her mother, and she looked very tired. It had been hard for Rosie, taking care of four children after her husband's death.

The youngest, Jakie, was almost nine now, and he needed a man's firm hand. Maybe there was a job for Jake after all.

He opened the door and Dog walked out, Jake close behind him.

Dog had already reached the stable door and stood waiting. Inside, Majesty stamped in the straw and whinnied his morning greeting, and Jake answered, with a catch in his voice.

"Hey, old feller!" It was all part of a never-failing ritual, so familiar that he rarely even thought about it.

He opened the stable door and the big Shire stood there, watching the man, ready for the daily procedure.

"GOODBYE, OLD FELLER"

Today, as Jake moved forward, was different. He wasn't going back to the cottage for his morning fry-up after the stable work was done. He was going across to Gaffer George's, where they were all waiting for him, to give him his last meal and speed him on his way.

"We're old, you and me," he said softly to the horse, and Majesty looked down at him, his brown eyes shining.

The stallion turned his huge body towards the manger, and bent to nose the dog. Dog lifted his nose in return.

Jake wanted to prolong it, and he wanted it over. Either way, it hurt.

Majesty was moved into the next stall and Jake began to sweep the dirty straw. He would leave the stable immaculate, even though there would be no horse to occupy it.

He lifted the straw into the barrow and carefully, slowly, took it across the yard to the midden. The sky was beginning to lighten now.

Dog lifted his head as Jake went back to the stable, then led Majesty back to his now clean stall.

There was nothing like the smell of clean hide and straw; of sweet hay. Majesty's warm tongue dropped into Jake's hand as he closed the half door. That had been a trick of the Emperor's, too.

"You daft old rogue," he said, and Dog's tail thumped in approval.

It was time for grooming.

Majesty reached for his hay-net, moving ponderously, and Jake was just in time to avoid the huge hoof. He needed to be spry on this job. For all his 72 years, he could still move fairly fast when he had to.

The one thing that wouldn't do his will was the wretched cough that sometimes racked him. The cottage was damp, but Rosie's home was modern and had central heating.

It was on the edge of the town; he would still be able to visit the farm, but . . .

Majesty, impatient, pushed against Jake, demanding full attention.

"You're spoiled rotten, you old rogue," Jake said, as was required of him. He wished he could be as unknowing of the future as the horse.

The last time.

Jake worked till the black hide gleamed, as it had on the day that Majesty had stood under the arc lights, and been greeted as Shire of the Year.

Prize after prize had been Majesty's in his young days.

"Easy, lad, easy." The words slipped out naturally as he worked. The last time. Jake swallowed, and worked on. It was the last time he would stand here, while the tail swished and the proud neck arched and the big hooves stamped impatiently in the straw.

"Nobody will ever say you left me looking like nobody had touched you," Jake said. It wouldn't matter so much later — today it still mattered.

The old horse wasn't going all that far, but he'd go dressed for his journey as he had always gone. He would be travelling in one of the big new transporters, as a special treat. But even so, he'd have his legs bandaged and he'd be rugged against draughts and cold air. His mane would be dressed and ribboned.

He'd go to his last home in the style he had been used to.

The Gaffer had come to tell Jake three weeks before.

He had to move with the times to keep the farm going, he had explained to Jake. It hadn't been the first time he'd tried to explain. He had to make the money work; he had to make the farm work; he had to move on, or go out of business.

Jake was part of the moving on.

H E stood now, the rug ready to put on the horse, wishing he were back in time. It was strange how heavy the modern rug was. It was a struggle now to lift it over the great back, to tighten the bands that held it; to ease it so that it lay smooth and unwrinkled, and comfortable.

Jake began to work again on the feather round the hooves, as it didn't yet shine with light as he wanted. He loved the feeling of the silken hair, alive against his hands. It was aching work, bent over, but everyone on the farm would be lined up to see Majesty go, and they would see him go with style.

The last time.

"Your grandad," Jake said, looking up at the animal towering above him, "it took hours to get him ready for a show. But when he was ready, he glistened all over. Proper royal, your grandad was. A great horse, with a great sense of dignity — not like you, you rascal."

Majesty looked down and suddenly Jake remembered him prancing in the meadow, frisking in the spring sunshine like a colt. Only last year, that was.

"'Morning, Jake!" Barney's voice said, from outside, then he put his head round the door.

"'Morning, Barney," Jake replied.

"Missus sent a flask of coffee; she'll be ready for you at eleven, she says. You will come?"

The coffee was scalding hot and very welcome. There was a nip of rum in it, just a taste, that lay sharp on the tongue.

"I'll come," Jake said.

"Jakie loves that horse," Barney said, patting the big animal.

Jake smiled at the thought of his small grandson. He remembered the child coming to see the big Shire, when Jakie was only two years old. He had stared up at the enormous creature that towered above him, and suddenly demanded imperiously, "Up!"

Jake had lifted him to the wide back and Jakie had sat there, with an expression of pure ecstasy on his face. The horse had stood as still as if he knew he was carrying a precious cargo.

"He's as horse crazy as you," Rosie had said.

Little Jakie loved the old scrapbooks, and they were brought out whenever he visited. The scrapbooks were almost a history of the Shire,

E

"GOODBYE, OLD FELLER"

going back to 1890 when the Gaffer's father had started the stud and Jake's own grandfather had been horsemaster.

They had added photographs of all the horses, and cut out the results from the farming papers; the story of the horse was there. The scrapbooks were a treasure-house of memory.

Jake put his hand up to stroke Majesty's neck. There was nothing more to be done, but he wanted to spin out every moment. The touch told Majesty he was the best horse in all the world, and he preened himself.

"History, that's what a horse is. And nobody knows today," Jake said. Dog sat up, roused by an odd tone in his master's voice. He saw the two men still drinking their coffee, and went back to sleep.

Jake swallowed the coffee and nodded to Barney. They had both heard the vet's old van chugging up the lane.

"Got a sick cow," Barney said, and left Jake to his memories.

Jake settled the rug again. He began to tidy the stable. He wanted to set the prize cards and rosettes neatly, even though the stable too would vanish.

He began to take them down, but it left the stable unfurnished and unfamiliar, an unhappy place that had never known it housed a champion. Jake pinned them back again, unwilling to leave the place derelict.

There were footsteps outside.

Jake wished they would leave him alone — a man needed time to adjust.

The Gaffer came into the stable, stooping to avoid hitting his head on the door. "I've rung to tell Rosie to meet you at Braddon's," he said. "Jakie's having the day off school to come with her. I thought you'd like to take the rugs and bandages off the old boy yourself, for the last time."

Jake nodded. He would like to, even though it would make his task harder.

"You can travel with him the way you used to do and Barney can follow in the Land-Rover with your baggage. It's not such a long journey."

Jake didn't want to think about the journey.

"Thank you," he said. "Is the cow all right?"

"Milk fever — she'll be fine," the Gaffer said. He paused, putting up a hand to stroke Majesty. Then he left Jake alone again.

JAKE had packed and he was ready, and there was nothing left to do. The cottage, stripped of its furnishings and of all memories of Nell, rejected him. He sat on the stool in the stable waiting for time to pass. The old horse stood patiently, as he so often stood, and Dog slept on.

"It's time, Jake," Barney said, obviously knowing how hard it was. Jake stood up wearily. He followed Barney across the yard. The sun had warmed the air, but the wind was still cool.

Dog trotted in front of them, knowing this ritual too. He was first into the big kitchen. The Gaffer laughed and gave him a piece of currant bun, as it was the old dog's last day as well.

"GOODBYE, OLD FELLER"

Jake came into the kitchen. Shire horses pranced on the walls — their pictures and their trophies were still in the heart of the house, and Marian would never part with them.

She smiled at Jake now. "I've made your favourite cake, Jake. Some to eat now, and some to take with you to remember us."

Jake couldn't speak. It was Nell's recipe that Marian had used — the rich cut-and-come-again cake, almost a Christmas cake, with a special tangy spice. It brought back memory, and took away speech.

"We had these done for you," the Gaffer said.

The two photographs were in matching silver frames.

One showed the massed display of trophies. There was every trophy that every Shire had ever won, with Jake in charge of them. The table was crammed. He could see the cup they'd won at the Royal Windsor Show, and the one from Peterborough. There were the smaller cups, too, from the local shows that were always such fun.

The other photograph made him catch his breath. He had expected to see Majesty in all his glory, but it wasn't that at all. It was an enlargement of little Jakie, no more than two years old, sitting on Majesty. Jake himself was looking up at him, holding on to the child.

"You never knew I was there," the Gaffer said.

Jake could say nothing. He picked up the two photographs and the wrapped cake, and walked out of the room, nodding to everyone. He stood just beyond the doorway, to recover.

The Gaffer came out, clapped him on the shoulder, then went in again.

His wife came out and kissed Jake's cheek, then Barney came and put an arm round his shoulder. He walked with him to the horsebox where Majesty stood, waiting, inside.

Jake followed the old routine without thinking.

For just an hour or so it seemed they were on their way to a show. Majesty would be dressed in his finery, to walk out in front of the admiring crowds, to take yet another trophy.

Memories crowded, and Jake dreamed of glory to come, following past glory. Then he saw the familiar turning that led to Braddon's and knew that his dreams had ended. This was indeed the last day.

He led Majesty out into the yard. Barney helped him remove the rug. It would not be needed now; nor would the bandages on the old Shire's legs that protected him from bumps and bruises in the box.

Braddon was a small man, now over-plump. His round face was merry.

"He'll be all right?" Jake asked, his voice forlorn.

Braddon nodded. "Put him in the little field, just there," he said. "That's just for the next few hours. He won't miss you for long — he won't have time."

The last time.

Jake led the old horse to the paddock. He was aware that Rosie had driven into the yard, aware of little Jakie calling to him, but he had no ears for them.

He led the old horse into his last home.

"GOODBYE, OLD FELLER"

"He's got a warm stable if he wants to get out of the cold," Braddon said. "I always take care of my old ones in their last days; he won't suffer, ever."

Jake nodded.

He patted the old horse and turned away. Suddenly, he heard the stamp of running hooves in the next field. He turned back, and saw Majesty lift his head and call, a stallion roar that held almost all the might of his earlier years.

Three heads looked curiously over the far gate.

The old Shire kicked up his hooves and galloped over to them, frisky as any youngster. One of the mares reached towards him and he nuzzled her then stood, his head across her neck.

"I'll put him in with them tomorrow," Braddon said. "He'll have the time of his life. My horses need a schoolmaster; the old ones are very good for them. I haven't had one since old Luke died — he was a grand teacher. Kept the young stock in order."

Jake looked at his old charge, and smiled. The old horse had shed years. He was young again in memory, if not in fact. The little mare leaning against him was one of the prettiest he had seen in years.

Jake turned to greet Jakie, who had come bounding across the yard.

"Mum's made a special supper for us; and have you got the scrapbooks? I want to look at them all tonight when we get home. And, Grandad, Mum said I wasn't to tell you yet, and don't tell her I have, but I've got a secret to tell you tomorrow."

Jake looked at his grandson. "I won't tell your mum you told me," he promised.

Jakie reached up and whispered.

"I've got a new pony! Mum wouldn't let me have one till I had you to teach me — she said it would be silly to have it without you there. You know so much and you can teach me all you know. His name's Prince Consort, only I call him Pippin."

Jake followed young Jakie to the car, which Barney was loading with all Jake's baggage.

"You'll be all right?" Barney asked, but Jake knew he was asking much more.

Jake turned to look at Majesty standing in the sunshine, the mare still nuzzling him.

He put a hand on little Jakie's head.

"Oh, yes," he said softly. "Don't worry, Barney. I'll be all right. We'll both be all right."

"Grandad, tell me how you saw King George the Fifth get his gold cup for his stallion, the one that's great-grandad to Majesty," Jakie said, as his mother drove them out of the farmyard.

Jake looked back. Majesty had not even turned his head.

"It was a long time ago, and I was a young man then," he began. Dog jumped from the floor to the seat and thrust an affectionate head against his master's knee. □

**Complete Story by
DI HARDIE**

FLYING FREE

ALICE took a last careful glance at herself in the mirror, checking her new suit and scarf. She was satisfied that she looked as good as she could. After all, she couldn't go to meet them in the same old clothes she had worn to wave them off more than two years before. No, that wouldn't do at all.

The handbag wasn't new, but it didn't matter. Ella and Michael had bought it for her and it matched nicely. Tucked inside were a comb, powder compact, and the little end of lipstick that had been with her for so long.

It would take more than two hours to get to the airport and a little freshening-up was bound to be needed by then. She did so want to look her best.

She had a last look round. The flat was perfectly tidy, but then it always was. There was no-one else

She loved her family and she certainly didn't want to be a burden to them. After all, they had their own hopes, their own dreams, their own plans for the future.

to make a muddle. Not that it mattered — they wouldn't be coming back here with her.

Under the circumstances we thought it best to go to Ella's parents, Michael had written. *But we shall be looking forward so much to seeing you at the airport.*

And she mustn't be late. Hastily she closed the flat door.

Old Mrs Patterson was busy sweeping out her corner shop. She smiled as she saw Alice.

"The big day!" She obviously wanted to talk and she had been

69

FLYING FREE

kind. It had been wonderful to use her telephone, to actually spend a few precious minutes speaking to Michael on the other side of the world. Perhaps Alice could spare a moment. As long as she didn't miss the train.

"You must be so excited." Mrs Patterson's face was rosy with interest. "How long are they here for?"

"Five weeks." It sounded a wonderfully long time. She refused to think beyond that, to the time when they were gone again. "First Michael has to spend three weeks on the course . . ."

"Oh, yes. The special photography." Mrs Patterson nodded eagerly. It wasn't every day one of her customers had a son and daughter-in-law arriving from New Zealand, and she had enjoyed every moment of the mounting excitement.

Giving Alice the use of her telephone so that she could be sure of the last-minute arrangements had been a small price to pay.

"Micro-photography." Alice was immensely proud of Michael's achievements. "He has to take pictures of all sorts of tiny little insects. It's for research, you know. He's quite a specialist in it.

"And now that they've brought out a new camera and new processes over here, his firm have sent him all the way over to learn about it. Then he has to order all the new equipment to be sent out to them . . ."

But Mrs Patterson wasn't listening. She frowned. "Are they going to stay with your daughter-in-law's parents all the time?" Her tone was frankly disapproving.

"Oh, no." Alice hastened to the defence. "Not all the time. They will be with Mr and Mrs Johnson for the first three weeks. While Michael is busy all day it's natural Ella should prefer to be with her own. When he's finished the course they'll be able to spend some time with me, I expect. Perhaps stay a night or two."

Mrs Patterson shook her head. She was a motherly little woman and she meant well. "I don't know how you let him go in the first place," she said sadly. "I've got three but it would break my heart to see any one of them go that far away."

"Well . . ." Briskly Alice pulled on her gloves. She could understand Mrs Patterson. Lots of others had said the same thing over the past two years. "He wanted to go. He had his heart set on it and so had Ella. And he had a very good job to go to."

"I know." Mrs Patterson was still shaking her head. "But when it's the only one you've got and it leaves you all alone . . ."

"It doesn't make any difference." Alice lifted her chin decisively. "You still have no right to tie them to your apron strings forever, have you?"

She thought about that as she hurried to the station.

Apron strings! Funny, but she couldn't ever remember actually using these words herself before. They were Tom's words. He had said them often and they had lingered on, held among the bitter-sweet memories of him she still kept tucked at the back of her mind.

Dear Tom. He had been an invalid when she had married him. She had known life would have its limitations for them, and she had known time might be short for him, but when tiny Michael had been born she had been sure no couple could have been happier.

"He's strong. Look at him!" Tom had marvelled delightedly over his precious son as he had cradled him in his arms.

"Alice, love, there will probably be lots of things we won't be able to give him, but at least, thank God, we've given him a strong, healthy body to start with. And we'll teach him to stand on his own sturdy little legs. No apron strings for him, eh, love?"

She had always tried to remember that. Tom had watched over his little son with careful pride for seven years, then she had been left to face the task alone. And she tried so hard to continue as Tom would have wanted. Whatever happened there were to be no apron strings.

T HE train was already in the station. Anxiously Alice scrambled into it and found a seat. Then gratefully she sat quietly until she had regained her breath. What if she had missed the train? What if she hadn't got to the airport in time to meet them? They would have waited, of course. Then perhaps they would have thought she had changed her mind, that she wasn't coming.

In the end, no doubt, they would have gone on to Ella's parents and from there Michael would have phoned Mrs Patterson to make sure she was all right. But she wouldn't have seen them . . . perhaps not for three whole weeks.

As she sat staring out of the carriage window, Alice resolutely tried to choke back a pang of jealousy. It wasn't Michael's fault, nor Ella's either. It was natural she should prefer to go to stay at her own parents' home.

They would expect it. Yet the Johnsons already seemed to have so much; another daughter, a son, a big house, two cars, no money worries . . .

She sighed. Michael and Ella had been married almost six months before he had been offered the job in New Zealand, yet she hardly knew the Johnsons.

They had only met at the lavish engagement party they had arranged, and three months later at the wedding.

Mr Johnson had an important job, while Mrs Johnson appeared to have a busy social life. Nothing like her own. Nothing at all.

Still, it would have been nice to have been invited back with Michael and Ella today. She could have spent a few hours with them, even if it was in someone else's home.

Then Mr Johnson could have driven her to the nearest railway station. She wouldn't have had any trouble finding her way home alone. Perhaps she could have stayed the night . . . been made to feel really at home . . .

She stopped herself abruptly. Funny, but every time she felt sorry for herself, or envious of others, her thoughts went flying back to Tom. He had hated envy and he had hated self-pity, he who could perhaps have been excused it.

"No, love." She could hear him still. "Envy never gained anyone anything. Only blinded them maybe to the blessings they already have."

Dear Tom. Dear gentle Tom. How delighted she had been that Michael had taken after him in so many ways. The same blue eyes, gentle, yet ready to light up with laughter. The same unruly mop of dark hair. The same bright smile. The same quiet reluctance to make her unhappy or to hurt her feelings.

Michael had been dating Ella for three months before he had brought her home.

"I had to be sure, Mum," he had said seriously. "I had to be sure she was the right one before I brought her home to you. Now I'm hoping you'll love her."

And she had loved Ella. Partly because Michael had loved her and partly because she had seemed a lot like the daughter she and Tom had once hoped for.

Certainly it had never occurred to her to object when Michael had told her he intended to ask Ella to marry him. It had seemed right, somehow, the natural sequence of things.

That was why the letter had surprised her so much. Mrs Johnson had felt they should wait — a year at least. Ella was still very young, and surely Michael ought to finish his studies. Perhaps if both families joined forces to object the young couple might see sense.

I am sure you will agree with my husband and me. The letter had been very confident. *Especially as Michael is all you have, and we understand that when he marries you will probably have to give up your house and move into a little flat somewhere.*

Alice looked out the window as the train sped swiftly through a station, but her thoughts were far away. She hadn't talked to anyone about that letter, not even Michael or Ella. They might have been hurt and unhappy and she hadn't wanted that.

It had taken her almost a week to write the reply. She did her best to explain carefully and politely how she felt, how she had always felt about Michael making his own decisions and standing on his own feet, just as Tom would have wanted him to.

The Johnsons had never replied.

Three months later, when Ella and Michael had become engaged, they had insisted upon giving a big lavish party. Relatives, friends, business associates, all gathered together at an expensive hotel near the Johnsons' home.

Michael had booked rooms for both of them because the Johnsons' home had been overflowing with relatives.

Ella had helped her to choose a pretty dress, and pinned an orchid on her, and kissed her before she came downstairs. Yet somehow she had felt ill-at-ease, a stranger among strangers, noticed only because she was Michael's mother.

It had been the same at the wedding.

Ella had looked so beautiful, and Alice had been so proud of Michael.

She had wanted to talk to someone about them, to tell someone how much she loved them both, how glad she was Michael had brought her a daughter like Ella, and how proud she was of Michael. But there hadn't been anyone. No-one close to confide in.

Old Dr Evans who had watched over Michael like a father hadn't been well enough to make the journey. And Mrs Thomas, who had known him since he was a baby, had been down with her asthma again. So there had been no-one. No-one she had felt at ease with.

The train sped through station after station. Carefully Alice checked her ticket, and tucked it into the front of her purse. Before long she would be getting off. The bus to the airport left from the station yard so there would be no problems. She would be in comfortable time to meet the plane.

THE bus was waiting. A host of other passengers boarded it too. Most of them carried luggage. Alice smiled at the middle-aged woman who settled herself beside her. "No. I'm not going anywhere. I'm meeting my son and daughter-in-law. They are coming from New Zealand."

"Oh, how wonderful for you." The woman was friendly. "And for them. I'll bet they will be over the moon to see you."

Alice nodded happily. Of course they would be. Michael would hug her and Ella would hold her tight and kiss her, and then they would talk. There would be so much to say.

Perhaps they would have a cup of tea — or a meal? That way, for an hour or so, she would have them all to herself, and . . .

The thought came out of the blue. She pushed it away, but it came back, and refused to be pushed aside. Why should she imagine that she alone would be meeting them? What about the Johnsons?

Alice sat very still, looking out of the bus window as it sped towards the airport. She had the feeling the woman beside her would have been happy to talk but suddenly she didn't want to.

Of course the Johnsons would be there. It was natural that they should be. They hadn't wanted Ella and Michael to go to New Zealand in the first place.

Mrs Johnson had been particularly upset. She had been angry and tearful and had told them she was sure there were plenty of opportunities for Michael in England, plenty of jobs, just as good as the one he was being offered on the other side of the world.

Alice sighed, remembering. Again and again Michael had come home sad and concerned after he and Ella had tried to reason with them.

"They just don't want us to go, Mum," he had said unhappily. "They think I should turn the job down. Ella's father got me on my own and had a long talk with me. He said he felt we weren't being fair to Mrs Johnson. She's dead set against all of it."

He had sighed and leaned his head against her as she hugged him. "What do you think, Mum? What should we do?"

She hadn't answered at once. She had thought of Tom, trying to

FLYING FREE

imagine what he would have wanted her to say.

"What do you and Ella want?" she had asked at last. "If there were just the two of you alone, with no-one else to consider, what would you do?"

Michael had looked into her face. "We want to go, Mum," he had said honestly.

She knew exactly what Tom would have thought. "No apron strings, love," he would have whispered. "Not for our boy."

"Well then," she had said at last. "It's your loves and your future. If you are sure enough of each other to take this big step together then I don't think anyone ought to try to stop you."

Six weeks later they had kissed her goodbye. She had stood alone at the airport and waved till they were out of sight. The Johnsons had not been there. Mrs Johnson had been too upset.

Alice had not seen them since. Each Christmas they had dutifully exchanged cards. The Johnsons' were big and expensive and specially printed, and hers were small but bright. Mrs Patterson didn't sell anything else in her corner shop.

Now, two years later, Ella and Michael were coming back and the Johnsons would be there to meet them. Of course they would.

Surely they must be just as thrilled as she was at this reunion? No doubt they would have come down by car and be ready to drive Ella and Michael home with them.

But at least she would see them. Resolutely Alice lifted her chin. This was no time to be sad, no time to be going back over the past.

Soon she would see her precious Ella and Michael. No matter who was watching, she would have a chance to kiss them and hug them and tell them how much she loved them and how much she had missed them.

RIGHT on time, the bus pulled up before the airport building. Alice knew she had a few minutes to spare before the flight would be due. Quickly she made her way through the crowded entrance, and, following the signs, climbed the stairs.

People were everywhere, jostling, hurrying, weighed down with luggage or shepherding young children; everyone seemed absorbed with their own problems.

At the entrance to the lounge she paused and stared round. It was crowded, every seat was occupied, and people stood about in little groups. But she could see no sign of the Johnsons.

The clock told her there were less than ten minutes to go. Suddenly she remembered the powder, the lipstick and the comb. She should have found a ladies' room and combed her hair and powdered her nose. There was still time.

But what if the plane were early? What if she missed them now? Tightly she gripped her handbag and waited.

Suddenly little knots of people began to trickle through the doors at the end. She knew they were coming. Ella and Michael were coming!

All at once it was hard to breathe. It was as though a great weight was

74

growing in her chest. Her cheeks began to warm and her eyes blurred.

Then suddenly they were there, both hugging and kissing her, practically squeezing the breath from her, and making the tears roll down her cheeks.

"Mum. Oh, Mum, it's good to see you!" She didn't know who said it. They were both talking at once. Talking and still hugging her.

"Come on. We've to see to our luggage, then we'll have a cup of tea."

They were whisking her away towards the sign which read "Passengers' luggage".

Alice stopped and shook her head. "Ella, your mother and father." She smiled through her tears as she straightened her hat. "In this crowd they'll have a job to find you. Perhaps you ought to wait a bit."

WHO CAN UNDERSTAND US?

Who can understand us, two passing ships at night,
That call out to each other when evening lights are bright?
We'll stop and drop our anchors and call to say hello,
while all the crew around us are sleeping down below.
We cannot be true strangers as we pass from shore to shore,
and spend each magic moment until the closing of the door.
But while we are together a tender loving breeze,
passes over both our lives like Autumn's falling leaves.
We know deep down our hearts are true, we've seen the path before,
instead of accepting how we feel we stumble then we fall.
Our feelings much too strong to hide we turn and walk away,
as we weigh our anchors finally we bid ourselves good day.

— D. B., Leics.

"No, Mum." Ella shook her head. She looked happy but tired and there were shadows under her eyes. "They couldn't get here. Mother is organising some big charity fête today and Dad has an important business meeting. They're going to try to meet us at the station. Now come on. I'm just dying for a cup of tea."

"No." Michael smiled. He looked happy, too. But older, and there was a gentle protectiveness about the way his arm rested for a moment about Ella's shoulders. "I'll see to the luggage. You two wait here."

Ella slid her hand into Alice's. "Best do as he says, Mum," she whispered. "He's been getting a little bit dominant lately." Her eyes twinkled. "But nice with it — of course."

Alice stared at her and suddenly she knew, though she wasn't quite sure how. Perhaps it was the happiness in Ella's face or the gentleness in Michael's. Or perhaps joy at the sight of them had tuned her to understanding. But she knew she was right. Ella was pregnant.

"Ella . . ." She stopped. This was their secret, something they would want to tell her in their own time. She just held Ella's hand very tightly.

Michael was gone only a few minutes. He came back carrying their suitcases. "Tea, Mum? Come on. A nice cup of tea then we can talk."

She went with them, still clinging tightly to Ella's hand. They found a table in the corner of the café and Michael set down the cases and smiled at his mother.

"I'll get the tea." He shook his head as she made to go with him to help. "No. You stay here, Mum. Stay with Ella. She's got something to tell you."

A LICE watched him as he picked his way through to the long self-service bar. He had almost reached it before she took her eyes off him. Ella was watching her. "Mum," she said softly. "It's so good to see you." Alice smiled. She was glad she had guessed, but even happier that she hadn't told them so. She didn't want to spoil it. Suddenly she felt very close to them.

"Michael said you had something to tell me," she said gently.

Ella nodded. She hesitated, and seemed to find it hard to begin.

Alice patted her hand. "You look very happy," she ventured. "Both of you."

Ella raised her eyes. "Oh, we are happy, Mum," she said earnestly. "We really are. You were right to encourage us to go. We've found a good life and Michael loves the work he's doing. He seems to have a marvellous future ahead of him. And we've made lots of wonderful friends, and . . ." Her voice tailed off. Her eyes searched Alice's. She smiled. "You've guessed, haven't you?"

Alice screwed her face and chuckled. Suddenly she couldn't resist it. "You're going to have a baby, aren't you?"

"Oh, Mum." Ella was laughing and crying at the same moment. "You guessed. I knew you would, I told Michael so. That's when he said he wanted me to be the one to tell you. He said it would be better coming from me first."

"Ella!" Alice chuckled. "Surely neither of you thought for a minute I wouldn't be thrilled?"

"No." Ella leaned across the table and took both her hands tightly in her own. "I didn't mean he wanted me to tell you about the baby. I meant he wanted me to be the one to ask you if you would come back to New Zealand with us.

"No, please, Mum." She shook her head and plunged on quickly. "Don't say a word until you've listened.

"I know it's sudden, and it's asking a lot of you, but . . . well, we would love you to come so much. We've been thinking about it for a long time. We have a lovely house, and Michael has already made all the enquiries. We could have a flat built on to the end of it. It would be small but very comfortable. You could live your own life, have your privacy, but you'd still be very close to us.

"Mum." She still held Alice's hands tightly. "Try to understand. The baby has just made us feel we want you all the more.

"We have everything out there . . . except family. I don't want to be selfish but I would like my children to have a really happy life, and to me that includes grandparents. Happy, loving grandparents they can turn to whenever they need them.

"Michael has told me all he remembers about his father. I only wish they could have him too. But they could have a grandma, to love them, and encourage them and guard all their secrets. You know what grandmas are like, I loved mine so much I thought I would never stop crying when she died.

"My mother seemed to have so many other things to take up her time, but Grandma was always there . . ."

Alice sat very still. Ella was still talking, but the words were blurring softly as understanding slowly throbbed through her. They wanted her to be with them. Ella and Michael wanted her.

"Ella, your parents?" Alice asked. "Your mother — what about her?"

Ella shook her head sadly. "I love Mother, of course, but her life is here. She has her social life and her friends. They are important to her. And work is important to Dad."

Ella was silent a moment, before continuing. "That's why we felt we ought to stay with them while we are here. Who knows? It could be the last time we see them. I hope not, but . . ."

"Have you told her?" Suddenly Alice realised that Michael was back. He put down the tea-tray and sat beside her.

"Well, Mum?" There was no mistaking his eagerness. "I know it must have come as a surprise. Perhaps we should have waited to tell you, but . . . well, we want you to come so much, and we only have five weeks here."

"Michael." Ella's voice was gentle. "Your mother needs time to think. Look, I'll pour the tea."

"It's funny." Alice stared at the teacup as Ella set it down in front of her. Later she would be able to think clearly, but now in her head there was only confusion. A lovely, happy confusion.

"Apron strings," she said softly. "I don't know whether you would remember, Michael, but there was one thing your father was always determined about. No apron strings."

"Mum!" Michael stared at her. "Oh, please don't misunderstand. Ella and I don't want to tie you to our apron strings, we know you are strong and capable. We know you can make a life for yourself here without us — you already have. We want you to come with us because we love you and because we feel we need you."

Alice drew a deep breath. And a wistful little tinge of regret trembled through her as she smiled. It would have been nice if Tom had been there. He had always had such a good sense of humour. It would have amused him to think of Ella and Michael trying to tie her to their apron strings.

But of course they weren't. He would have understood that. And she knew he would have been happy for her. She knew he would have approved. □

WELCOME

"Nothing has changed," they said.
No, she thought, only my whole world . . .

THROUGH the window Anna could see the day outside was dark and overcast, reflecting her mood as she stood before Matron in her office. The room, bright with artificial light, was stuffy from overheating.

"The only part-time post I can offer you at present, Mrs Jones, is in Casualty."

"Oh!" She couldn't hide the disappointment in her voice, but she hoped the other woman wouldn't recognise the note of fear that was there, too.

"Is there nothing else?" she asked, this time trying to disguise her emotions, especially the desperation she felt.

"I'm afraid not. But I see from your application that you've worked in Casualty before," Matron was saying, as she turned over some papers on her desk, and looked up at Anna questioningly.

"That's right, but . . . I'd rather not work there again." Even the thought of the mounting pile of bills at home couldn't persuade her otherwise.

"I see," Matron said, but of course Anna knew that she didn't. "The only other vacancy is a full-time post on Female Surgical."

"Full-time?" Anna was daunted at the very idea, but she knew there was really no alternative. "What . . . what would the hours be?" she heard herself asking.

"Five whole days a week, late or early shift, depending on how Sister works the off-duty." She beamed at Anna across the wide-topped desk, confident this would be suitable.

How could she possibly leave Sally for five whole days a week? Early shifts she'd have to leave the house before her baby daughter was even awake. Late shifts would mean she'd not be home in time to put her to bed. Yet with her mother's help she knew she could overcome that side of it. She would have to! But she needed time to think, adjust.

"Could I . . . could I let you know, Matron?"

"Of course, Mrs Jones." The woman consulted her large desk diary.

"Let's see . . . Friday of this week? If I've not heard from you by then, I'll assume you've decided against it."

A Complete Story by Frances Fitzgibbon

78

Anna made her way back to the porter's lodge, where Sally was still asleep in her pram under the watchful eye of the elderly head porter. He rose from the wooden bench outside the lodge to greet Anna as she arrived.

"Good as gold she's been, Nurse Hollis. Be pleased to look after her any time."

"Thanks, Archie." She didn't correct him on his use of her maiden name. She supposed she'd always be Nurse Hollis to him.

"How did you find the new Matron, then?" He watched her through his thick-lensed glasses.

"She seems all right," Anna said carefully.

"Offer you a job, did she?"

Anna nodded by way of reply. "Part-time Casualty or full-time Female

WELCOME BACK

Surgical," she said in a flat voice.

"Casualty." He said the word warily, then turned away to wheel Sally's pram on to the concrete drive. "You won't be wanting that." He made the statement seem light. And suddenly Anna couldn't trust herself to speak. Instead she bent over her daughter's pram so that Archie wouldn't see the tears that had sprung to her eyes.

"But you'd be all right on Female Surgical, working in young Dr Crow's team," Archie was now saying, glad to be past a difficult subject. "Besides, weren't you two friends . . .?"

So Ian Crow was still here. Dear, dependable Ian who'd quietly faded out of her life as her dynamic Steve had come bursting in.

A knocking on the inside of one of the windows of the Lodge caused her to look up. Archie's wife was there holding back the net curtain, smiling and waving.

"It's been the making of her over the years," Archie spoke softly, smiling back at his wife.

He must have felt Anna's questioning glance, for he went on, "Other folk's bairns. Like little Sally here."

Then she remembered how hospital talk had it that he and his wife had lost their only child. Ever since, they'd offered a kind of child-minding service to all the staff at St Mary's.

She waved back to Archie's wife then turned to go.

"Be seeing you then," Archie called after her. "Remember, any time you want to bring the bairn . . ."

She forced a smile and raised an arm in farewell and acknowledgement of his offer.

GLAD to have you back with us," was all Sister on Female Surgical said by way of welcome on Anna's first day back. "Thank you, Sister," she replied, with more calmness than she felt.

"I'm sure I don't need to show you the ropes," Sister went on. "There's not been much change since you left."

Anna flinched. Oh, how she wished she could say that about her life.

Even now she shivered with horror at the memory of that day. The shock of the phone call . . . an accident . . . her Steve . . . Casualty Department. Like flashes from an old film reel she recalled the blur of her journey to St Mary's, the mounting fear as she waited for word and the heart-stopping news that left no hope at all.

But it was Monday morning and the ward was a hive of activity. And there was no time to dwell on such thoughts.

She was dressing a wound in the afternoon of that first day when the sound of an ambulance siren came to her ears.

She froze, the roll of sticking plaster in one hand, and listened, waiting as the sound came nearer.

"What's wrong, Nurse?" asked the middle-aged woman whose wound she'd been attending.

"Nothing." Her voice trembled. "I'm sorry." She continued with the task in hand, barely aware of what she was doing.

As the days wore on, she tried so hard to quell the terrible surge of fear that occurred every time she heard that siren. Each time she failed.

Her first real encounter with Ian Crow didn't come until the end of that first week, when she had to accompany him on his round.

It was a strange feeling, meeting him again. After all that had happened in her life, his had remained almost the same. Here they were working together again and it seemed to Anna that her life had turned full circle, that however reluctantly, she was starting all over again.

She felt a little shy, afraid to speak first. But then she didn't have to.

"How are you, Anna?" he asked, in the same kind voice she remembered.

She tried hard to smile naturally.

"I'm fine." Looking up at him was difficult, but when she did it was obvious he was waiting for her to say a little more.

"Things are still a little difficult, but at least I have Sally." And she just couldn't keep the quaver from her voice.

"How old is she now, Anna?" he asked gently, when she lowered her head again.

"She'll be one next month."

"With working full-time you can't see much of her."

"I see as much of her as I can," she snapped, more sharply than she'd intended.

"Do you have to?" he asked gently. "Work full-time, I mean."

"I'd prefer part-time . . . but . . . there are no posts." She pushed a folder of case notes into his hand in an effort to avoid further searching questions.

"Just a minute . . ." He drew his brows together, wrinkling up his forehead. "Isn't there one in Casualty, Sister . . . ?"

"Yes, there is," Anna interrupted. "But I don't want Casualty."

"I see." His voice as always was quiet, but she knew he'd guessed everything she was thinking.

As he watched her, she suddenly remembered the first time she'd seen him and how impressed she'd been by his earnest, gentle approach to friends and patients alike.

Taking a breath, she tried to think of the right words to make up for her sharpness but by then he had turned away and moved towards the first patient.

By the end of that first week back, Anna closed her eyes and mentally tried to take stock. She'd missed Sally desperately, especially on the late shift when she was already tucked up in bed on her arrival home. Watching her mother's joy at having her granddaughter to herself was a small compensation. But she had to continue . . .

The meeting with Ian was another niggle on her conscience. Since then, he'd been as pleasant as ever, but distant.

One day, she had to go down to Casualty to accompany a new patient up to the ward. She wavered on the threshold, painful memories

F

obliterating all else. Why couldn't Sister have sent someone else?

"Nurse Hollis!" It was Archie, beckoning her from the doorway to the Emergency Room. She pretended not to hear. They couldn't make her go in there.

Relief flooded through her just then as a Sister bustled out of the room into the corridor, wheeling a trolley bearing an ashen-faced patient. She came towards Anna.

"Female Surgery?" she enquired.

Anna nodded and tried to concentrate on the instructions Sister was giving her.

"How's wee Sally?" Archie asked from his steering position at the foot of the trolley, once they were on their way.

"She's fine thanks, Archie."

"The missus was just sayin', you know . . ."

But Anna wasn't listening any more, simply giving her full attention to her patient, relieved she was leaving Casualty behind.

IT wasn't too long before she found herself doing another round with Ian Crow. He seemed a little more at ease with her and surprisingly she felt quite relaxed in his company.

She was remaking a patient's bed, after Ian's examination, when she suddenly straightened, a look of fear on her face.

Noticing the panic on her face, Ian drew her away from the patient.

"What's wrong?" he asked in a concerned voice.

"Nothing, I'm fine." It annoyed and irritated her that he had noticed something was wrong. But he couldn't know it was the sound of an ambulance siren and its eerie signal that had interrupted the peace of the ward, and she wouldn't tell him.

"You sure you're all right?" he moved nearer her.

"Yes." She turned her back, anxious that he shouldn't recognise her fear.

"Dr Crow!" Sister's voice was full of urgency. "Casualty's put out a call for you."

Anna watched his disappearing figure as he fled down the corridor, the tails of his open white coat billowing like a sail behind him. She listened with bated breath, for it seemed that as one siren ceased, another was taking up its cry.

Then all was quiet and she filed away the case notes, noting how her fingers shook.

"Nurse Jones!" it was Sister. "There's a bit of a crisis in Casualty and they'd like you down there."

Anna stood rooted to the spot, every nerve in her body taut. She couldn't . . . Surely they wouldn't make her . . . ?

For what seemed like minutes, but could only have been seconds, Anna stood there. She felt Sister watching her and thought of Ian Crow already down there. He must have asked for her.

Growing fear increased her anger, and in that moment she hated him!

The strength of the emotion rocked her for an instant. She hadn't felt such anger since Steve's death.

"Nurse!" Sister's voice broke into her thoughts. "They need you. Quickly!"

Miraculously then, some inner force seemed to nudge her into action. Hardly aware of what she was doing, her body began to move with a speed short of running.

Down the flight of stairs she fled and on towards Casualty. She saw immediately that the red light was on above the large double doors leading into the Emergency Room.

A T first sight of the harrowing scene under the glaring lights, Anna's heart thumped painfully against her breast, and her eyes misted with painful memory.

Then, for the briefest of seconds, Ian Crow glanced up and his eyes met hers. It was all she needed. After only a brief word from Sister, unobtrusively, she became once more a part of a team.

Unlike her beloved Steve, he too a road casualty, an element of luck was on the side of these young people. Eventually all three were dragged back from death.

When finally it became time to hand them on to the furthering care of ward staff, Anna breathed an exhausted sigh, realising that for once in her fatigue, she no longer felt like crying.

"You did all right there, Nurse Hollis," a familiar voice behind her spoke as she remained to clear up.

She spun round with a surprised smile, "Archie!"

"First time's always the worst," he said quietly, proceeding with his task of checking the oxygen cylinders. "It'll get easier from now on. That's what me and the missus found anyway."

There was nothing for Anna to say and the comfortable silence that fell between them felt warm and satisfying.

After Archie had gone and she was re-stocking the last of the emergency trays, the doors behind her were pushed open.

"You did it, Anna." The voice was gentle but full of pride.

She turned slowly to face Ian. There was no doubt he was tired, yet she could sense his relief at the change in her.

His presence here in this room was like a warm blanket on a winter's night. Any anger she had felt was long since gone.

Yes, she'd done it — but only with his assistance. She smiled then, knowing with a growing certainty that for a short time she had set her grief aside, had at last come to terms with it.

"Thank you," she whispered, in a voice so low she couldn't be sure he had heard it.

But his eyes told her he had.

"You're a good doctor," she told him. And to herself she added, and a very special man.

Perhaps one day she would tell him. □

Materials Required – Of **Littlewoods Double Knit,** 1 x 100 gram ball in grey; washable toy stuffing; pieces of pink, black and white felt; one pair of 3¼ mm (No. 10) knitting needles; small amount of pink yarn for soles (optional) and tail.

For best results it is essential to use the recommended yarn. If you have difficulty in obtaining the yarn, write direct, enclosing a stamped, addressed envelope to the following address for stockists: Andrea Wood, Littlewoods Stores, Atlantic Pavilion, Albert Dock, Liverpool L70 1AD.

Measurement – Height, 29 centimetres, *11½ inches approximately.*

Tension – 26 stitches and 36 rows to 10 centimetres, *4 inches,* measured over stocking-stitch using 3¼ mm needles.

Abbreviations – **K** – knit; **P** – purl; **st.(s)** – stitch(es); **st.-st.** – stocking-stitch; **tog.** – together; **cm** – centimetres.

84

JUMBO

Knit our big, cuddly elephant. She's sure to find a place in everyone's heart.

BODY (Left Half)

*Cast on 17 sts. and work 8 rows in st.-st.

Increase 1 st. at beginning of next and following 2 alternate rows, then at same edge on next 4 rows – 24 sts.

Break off yarn and leave these sts. on a spare needle.

Cast on 28 sts. and work 8 rows in st.-st.

Increase 1 st. at end of next and following 3 alternate rows, then at same edge on next 2 rows, ending with a knit row – 34 sts.

Next row – P34, cast on 9 sts., P24 from spare needle – 67 sts. Increase 1 st. at end of next row and at same edge on following 3 rows – 71 sts.

Leave sts. on spare needle, do not break off yarn.*

Cast on 8 sts.

Increase 1 st. at each end of next 8 rows, ending with a purl row – 24 sts.

Break off yarn.

Knit the 71 sts., cast on 3 sts., then knit 24 sts. from needle, increasing 1 st. at end – 99 sts.

Purl 1 row.

Increase 1 st. at end of next and following 2 alternate rows – 102 sts.

Purl 1 row.

Next row – K90, cast off next 5 sts., K4, K2 tog.

Continue on last 6 sts., decrease 1 st. at each end of next 2 rows – 2 sts.

Cast off.

With wrong side facing, rejoin yarn to remaining 90 sts., P2 tog., purl to end.

Decrease 1 st. at end of next and following alternate row.

Decrease 1 st. at beginning of following row – 86 sts.

Work 3 rows.

Increase 1 st. at beginning of next and every following 4th row until there are 90 sts., then every 3rd row until there are 94 sts., ending with a purl row.

Continued overleaf.

85

JOLLY

Continued from previous page.

Work 4 rows straight.

Decrease 1 st. at beginning and increase 1 st. at end of next row.

Work 3 rows.

Repeat last 4 rows twice more.

Decrease 1 st. at beginning of next row. Purl 1 row.

Decrease 1 st. at each end of next and following 6 alternate rows, ending with a knit row – 79 sts.

Next row – P2 tog., purl to end.

Knit 1 row.

Repeat last 2 rows once more.

Decrease 1 st. at beginning and end of next row – 75 sts.

Cast off 2 sts. at beginning of next 2 rows, 3 sts. at beginning of next row, 2 sts. at beginning of next row, 4 sts. at beginning of next 2 rows, 5 sts. at beginning of next row, 4 sts. at beginning of next row, 6 sts at beginning of next row and 5 sts at beginning of next row – 38 sts.

Cast off.

Work right half to match, reversing all shaping.

UNDERBODY (Right Half)

Work as for left half body from * to *.

Decrease 1 st. at beginning of next row and at the same edge on following 4 rows.

Purl 1 row.

Decrease 1 st. at beginning of next row – 65 sts.

Work 2 rows.

Cast off.

Work left half to match, reversing all shaping.

EARS (Right Ear)

Cast on 9 sts. and knit 1 row.

Increase 1 st. at each end of next 3 rows.

Cast on 2 sts. at beginning and increase 1 st. at end of next row.

Purl 1 row.

Repeat last 2 rows twice more.

Increase 1 st. at each end of next row and increase 1 st. at beginning of following alternate row.

Purl 1 row.

Increase 1 st. at beginning of next row.

Increase 1 st. at each end of next row.

Work 3 rows.

Increase 1 st. at end of next row.

Work 4 rows straight.

Increase 1 st. at end of next row.

Work 1 row.

Increase 1 st at end of next row.

Cast on 3 sts. at beginning of next row.

Work 2 rows.

Decrease 1 st. at beginning of next row.

Work 3 rows.

Decrease 1 st. at each end of next and following 2 alternate rows.

Decrease 1 st. at beginning of next row.

Decrease 1 st. at each end of next 2 rows.

Cast off 3 sts. at beginning and decrease 1 st. at end of next row.

Decrease 1 st. at each end of next row.

Cast off 3 sts. at beginning of next 2 rows.

Cast off.

Work left ear to match, reversing shaping.

86

JUMBO

TRUNK END

Cast on 19 sts. and work 5 rows in st.-st.

Decrease 1 st. at each end of next and every following 5th row until 7 sts. remain.

Cast off.

BODY GUSSET

Cast on 8 sts. and work 2 rows in st.-st.

Increase 1 st. at each end of next and following 3 alternate rows, then every 3rd row until there are 24 st., every 4th row until there are 36 sts., and then every 6th row until there are 44 sts.

Work 11 rows.

Decrease 1 st. at each end of next and every 4th row until 30 sts. remain, every 3rd row until 24 sts. remain, then every alternate row until 2 sts. remain. Cast off.

TAIL

Cast on 18 sts. and work 4 rows in st.-st.

Cast off.

TO MAKE UP

Join head and trunk seams.

Join seam of underbody, leaving an opening for stuffing, and sew to lower edges of body.

Sew on end of trunk.

Sew body gusset in place, joining wide cast-on edge to underbody and ending at back of head.

Stuff body and stitch up opening.

Cut out soles in pink felt and sew to ends of legs. (If knitted soles preferred, see below.)

Cut out same shapes as ears in pink felt and sew to ears. Sew ears to head.

Cut out eyes in white and black felt and sew to head.

Cut out a strip of black felt for mouth and sew in place.

Make a small fringe in pink yarn and sew to end of tail, roll tail with purl side outside and join long seam, then sew to body.

Cut out toenails in white felt and sew to ends of legs.

KNITTED SOLES

(If you prefer you can knit the soles instead of using felt.)

Front Feet

Cast on 4 sts., knit 1 row.

Increase 1 st. at each end of next 3 rows and following 3 alternate rows.

Work 3 rows.

Increase 1 st. at each end of next row.

Work 5 rows.

Decrease 1 st. at each end of next and following 2 alternate rows, then every row until 4 sts. remain.

Cast off.

Make another sole to match.

Back Feet

Cast on 4 sts., knit 1 row. Increase 1 st. at each end of every following alternate row until there are 12 sts.

Work 3 rows.

Increase 1 st. at each end of next row.

Work 3 rows.

Decrease 1 st. at each end of next and every following alternate row until 4 sts. remain.

Cast off.

Make another sole to match. ∎

White Lace

Diane's mother had worn the christening gown, Diane had worn it and now it was Emma's turn. It all seemed so simple . . .

As soon as Sam Anderson put his key in the lock he sensed trouble. This evening there was no glad cry of welcome from his wife, Diane, no delicious cooking smells wafting from the kitchen.

Then he heard a deafening wail, and guessed at once that his new little daughter, Emma, was far from happy.

As a husband of almost 18 months' standing, a father to boot, Sam prided himself that as far as his women folk were concerned, there wasn't much he didn't know.

He found his family in the tiny nursery where a harassed Diane was walking up and down, the baby in her arms.

"Well, and how are my girls?" he cried cheerily.

Both regarded him stonily. Emma's minute lower lip quivered as she stopped crying just long enough to eye the new arrival without enthusiasm. Then she opened her mouth and roared again.

"I don't know what's the matter with her," Diane complained. "She's been a little monster today."

"Well," Sam said soothingly, "you look as if you've had about enough for the moment, love. How about letting old Dr Spock here have a go?"

Gratefully Diane passed her noisy little daughter over, and Sam held her against his shoulder, her tiny pink face close to his own.

"You know if you could bottle it, you'd make a bomb," he mused, gently muzzling Emma's neck.

"Mmmm?" Diane was rapidly picking up the bedtime debris from the floor.

"This marvellous baby smell," he went on. "I should say it's five per cent talcum, a dash of baby lotion, just a whiff of clean nightie, and ninety per cent. Emma."

"Hmmmm." Diane responded darkly. "Half an hour ago I don't think you'd have been quite so delighted."

At that moment Emma favoured her doting parents with a ladylike but unmistakable burp.

"There you are," Sam said triumphantly, "I thought it was wind. I don't think you'll have any more trouble now, Mrs Williams. She should be asleep in, let me see, about five minutes."

"You —" Diane retorted with a smile "— are about as insufferable as that daughter of yours. I don't suppose we'll ever hear the last of it. I'll just go and do something about supper if you'd like to put her down."

Sam continued to rock his drowsy little daughter for a bit longer. He still found himself smiling like an idiot every time he looked at this miniature replica of Diane.

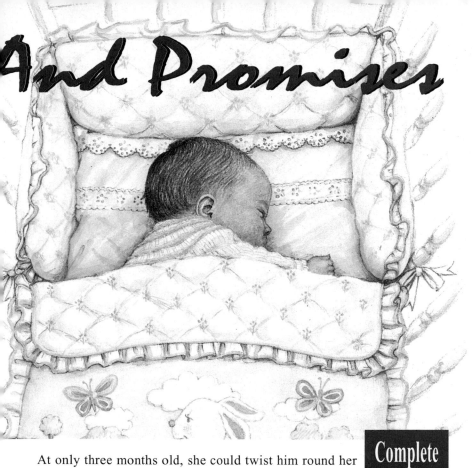

And Promises

Complete Story by BETTY PUTTICK

At only three months old, she could twist him round her small finger, a situation he found entirely satisfactory.

Later, as they sat eating supper, Sam noticed that Diane was quieter than usual.

Obviously there was something on her mind, and he knew her well enough to be sure that she wouldn't be able to bottle it up for long.

It was while they were washing-up together that she suddenly blurted it all out.

"Oh, Sam, what am I going to do?"

"Give me a clue," he suggested. "You're not still worrying about Emma, are you? She's bound to cry sometimes."

"Oh no, it's not that. Your mother asked us round today." Diane began. "She said she had a surprise for me. Oh, Sam, she really is great. Do you know what she's done?

"She's made this beautiful christening gown for Emma to wear next Sunday. It's simply gorgeous, all white lawn and little tucks and lace." Her eyes filled with tears.

He took her in his arms.

89

WHITE LACE AND PROMISES

"Hey, come on," he said. "It can't be that bad. What did you want her to wear?"

Diane's lovely blue eyes blinked away the tears and she managed to laugh.

"Oh, Sam, can you ever be serious? The point, in case you've forgotten, is that my gran rang up last week after we'd set the christening date, and reminded me that she has the family christening robe all ready for the great event!

"Apparently I wore it for my christening, and so did my mother, when she was a baby. So, of course, Gran's all set to have a third generation arrive at the font in it.

"I couldn't disappoint her, could I? But I can't disappoint your mum either. It's a nightmare."

Sam's smile faded.

"We should have had twins," he said, in an attempt to lighten the situation.

Diane didn't even smile.

"So what did you say to Mum?" he asked. "You don't mean you didn't tell her?"

"How could I when she'd put so much time and love into making this gown for Emma? You know how good she is at needlework." She sighed.

"I chickened out. I just gave her a big hug and said it was perfect."

"No chance of putting Gran off, I suppose?"

They both knew the answer to that. The very idea of telling Gran that her first great-grandchild would not require the family christening robe was not a thought either Sam or Diane cared to dwell upon.

"Well, let's sleep on it," Sam suggested at last. But it was a restless night for both of them.

"Don't worry, love," Sam said as he set off for work. "We're bound to think of something."

But time went by, and as the christening date got nearer, Diane looked pale, and there were shadows under her eyes.

"It's no good," she told Sam. "I'll just have to tell your mother about it. I can't bear to hurt her after all the trouble she's gone to, but I know she'll understand that we can't upset Gran either.

"It means so much to her that Emma should be christened in the family heirloom. That's why she's cherished it all these years."

THAT afternoon Diane changed Emma and put her in the pram for the short walk to her mother-in-law's house. She found herself dawdling along slowly, admiring other people's gardens, looking in the shops, anything to put off her arrival. All too soon, however, she turned into the pretty tree-lined road where Sam's parents lived.

"Hello," she called.

"Oh, hello, Diane, what a nice surprise." Sam's mother came hurrying into the kitchen.

"As a matter of fact I was just on my way round to see you! Come along in, I'll just put the kettle on and we'll have a cuppa."

"Emma's asleep in the pram," Diane said, "so I've left her in the garden."

She wandered into the comfortable sitting-room, and was staring rather glumly out of the window when Jill bustled in with a tray of tea things. She looked keenly at her daughter-in-law.

"You look rather tired, Diane," she said. "Has Emma been giving you some bad nights?"

"Not really. But there is a bit of a problem I want to talk to you about."

"Let me guess." She smiled. "I don't suppose it has anything to do with a certain young lady with too many christening robes?"

"How in the world . . . ?"

"Well, yesterday when I was shopping I met your gran, and she told me about this family heirloom . . .

"That's why I was coming round. I guessed you'd be worrying."

"If only you knew . . ." Diane cried with relief. "I've been lying awake at night wondering how I could possibly solve the problem of two gowns and only one baby. I thought you'd be so disappointed."

"Well," her mother-in-law admitted, "I am, just a bit, but an heirloom's an heirloom. Obviously Emma must wear it. It means such a lot to your gran, bless her."

"You know," Diane said, giving her a hug. "You really are super. Only you could be Sam's mother."

That evening, Sam was almost bowled over by his exuberant wife when he returned home.

"Sam," she cried, "did you know you've got a marvellous mother?"

"Well," he said modestly, "she was the best I could get at the time. Something tells me we've solved the christening gown problem."

"She met Gran! Oh, Sam, she's been so understanding about it. I can't tell you what a relief it is!"

"There's no need," Sam said with feeling. "Does this mean we can get some sleep at nights now?

"After all," he laughed, "any day now I'll have to start worrying about what Emma's going to wear at her wedding."

T HE next day Diane's mother arrived with Gran in tow, the old lady clutching a box. "Here it is," she cried excitedly, as Diane kissed her. "I've brought Emma's christening gown. She's going to look lovely in it, just as you did dear — and of course your mother too.

"I made it for Mary. Couldn't do it now, my sight's not what it was.

"But I almost had to let you down, Diane." The old lady chuckled. "I knew I'd put the dress away in a safe place, but after all this time I'd forgotten where it was! But your mother found it just before we came."

Diane and her mother exchanged smiles, but as soon as Gran had gone into the garden to see Emma in her pram, Mary whispered hurriedly.

WHITE LACE AND PROMISES

"Don't say anything when you see the christening gown."

"What do you mean?"

"You'll see when you open the box. After all, I suppose I should have expected it, it's been put away since your christening and . . ."

At that moment Gran came back.

"Well come on, you two," she cried briskly. "What are we waiting for?"

The box was tied up with string, and as Diane fumbled with the knot, Gran's impatience grew.

"Cut it, dear," she urged. "We haven't got all day."

Diane snipped the string and opened the lid.

The musty smell rising from the once beautiful dress told its own tale.

Mildew stains blotched the delicate fabric and many a moth had found the perfect place to give its offspring a nourishing start in life.

"Hold it up," Gran demanded. "I haven't seen it since you were christened, Diane. I expect it will want a press and perhaps some new ribbons," the old woman continued, "but you can see to that, can't you, dear? Come on now, let's have a proper look at it."

As Diane hesitated, her mother, unnoticed by Gran, put a warning finger to her lips. Then she carefully picked up the dress and held it, bunching the material to hide the damage. Gran peered over her glasses.

"Careful, Mary," she cried. "You'll spoil it, holding it all crumpled up like that. I can hardly see it."

Meet A Pet

Here's a special selection of your favourite pet pictures.

"Who's this little visitor?" says Suki, the much-loved pet of Mrs M. Hilsdon of Granborough.

Suki

Jasper

Miss A. Willstrop of York says that Jasper would rather not help with the decorating!

At that moment, with perfect timing, Emma awoke, and in the pleasure of cooing over her great-granddaughter, Gran's attention was diverted enough for Diane to pop the dress back in the box and put it out of sight.

She groaned inwardly. What were they going to do now?

As Diane and her mother washed-up the tea things, they held a whispered conference.

"She'd kept it in a drawer in the damp back bedroom, wrapped up in tissue paper," Mary explained. "I was horrified when I went up to get it.

"On the spur of the moment I put it in a box so that she wouldn't see it before we came. I couldn't think what else to do at the time."

"Well, she'll have to know, won't she?" Diane said. "There's no way Emma can wear it like that."

"But she's been talking so much about Emma wearing it, she'll be so upset. We'll just have to think of something."

"Where have I heard that before?" Diane sighed. "We're back to square one."

On impulse, she telephoned her mother-in-law and when Sam arrived home, he found his wife and mother, their heads close together, over the table on which Gran's heirloom and the new gown made by Jill lay side by side. No-one greeted him.

"Don't tell me . . ." he began. But Diane merely waved a hand in the direction of the oven, and returned to her absorbed discussion.

Snoopy

Mrs D. Roberts of Wellingborough's cat, Snoopy, fancies herself as the next Steve Davis!

Whisky

Luckily, this is as far as Whisky gets to the tropical fish, says Mrs J. Rhodes of Ossett.

As an afterthought, she went over and kissed him on top of his head.

"Sorry," she said briefly, "but it's a desperate situation."

She returned to find her mother-in-law looking more cheerful.

"Look," she said. "I think I know what we can do. Luckily the lace round the bottom of Gran's dress is almost perfect. I could easily transfer it to the one I've made."

"But it smells so fusty," Diane objected.

"Don't worry, I'll wash it first. As you can see, the dresses are fairly similar in style. I'll just add some more lace to the bodice of the new one, and providing we don't let Gran get a really close look on Sunday, with any luck she'll never know it isn't her dress.

"After all, her sight's not too good now, bless her, and she's not going to remember every detail after all this time, is she?"

"Probably not. It's a chance we'll have to take," Diane answered doubtfully. "But you've only got a couple of days before the christening. I feel awful letting you in for all this."

"Thank goodness I'd already made the other dress or we really would have been on the spot," her mother-in-law laughed.

"Come on, Diane, cheer up. If Gran gets too inquisitive, we'll breathe on her glasses!"

S TANDING by the church font the following Sunday with her loved ones around her, Diane relaxed. It had all worked out very well really, and she hadn't had to disappoint anybody in the end.

There was Gran, looking smart in a new rose-trimmed hat, beaming happily to see her little great-granddaughter wearing what she fondly believed to be the family christening robe.

And dear Jill, all her beautiful work hadn't gone to waste either.

The deep sonorous tones of the vicar as he began the service brought her back to earth.

Until that moment, Emma too had been dreaming peacefully. Now she woke with a start as the cold water touched her forehead.

Two bright blue eyes opened wide, one small pink mouth opened even wider, and she screamed, and screamed. So loud that even Gran noticed.

"That's right." The old lady nodded with satisfaction. "Babies should cry at a christening. It lets the Devil out."

At the christening party, Diane circulated, attending to her guests. Sam was standing by the french windows, holding Emma, and Diane glanced round warily for Gran.

Too late, she noticed the little figure, rose hat firmly placed on her white head, resolutely approaching Sam and Emma.

"It'll be all right, don't worry," Jill soothed. "Come and have a piece of christening cake before it's all gone."

"And how about a piece for the proud father," Sam's voice said behind them, "and another little slice for Gran?"

"Sam!" Diane turned anxiously. "I thought you had Emma."

"It's all right, Gran's taken over."

"I really don't believe this!" Diane cried. "We've been so careful all day seeing that Gran didn't get a good look at Emma's gown, and now you've probably blown the whole thing."

"Rubbish," Sam said unrepentantly, "She was dying to hold Emma, and why shouldn't she? Look at them both."

They looked across at Gran, sitting blissfully rocking Emma.

"Here you are, Gran," Sam said, walking over. "How about one more piece of christening cake?"

"Put it down on the table there, dear." She chuckled. "I just want another little cuddle with Emma. It's not every day I get the chance."

"It's been a lovely day, Gran, hasn't it?" Diane said.

"Lovely, dear," the old lady replied. "But I'm a bit tired now. If Mary's ready, I think I'll be getting home."

With great gentleness she released Emma's hand.

"You're a lucky man, Sam," she said, smiling up at him.

"'Bye, Gran." Diane gave her a kiss as the old lady turned to go.

"Bless you, too, love," Gran replied. "To think you and Sam's mother went to so much trouble to save hurting my feelings. Me and my heirloom!" she snorted.

"Gran!" Diane cried in dismay. "We hoped you hadn't noticed!"

"Well," Gran smiled. "I did think the old dress looked even better than I remembered. Then when we were all coming out of the church, I heard Mrs Anderson's neighbour and another lady admiring it, so I had to listen, hadn't I?

"They said the lace from the old family christening robe finished off the dress Jill made so beautifully, and how lucky it was the moths hadn't ruined that, too, like the rest of it." Her voice faltered.

"When you get as old as I am," she went on quietly, "sometimes you feel a bit out of things. I just wanted to help with Emma's christening, but all I did was give you a lot of work."

"Don't be upset, Gran." Diane put her arm round the old lady's shoulders.

"We've still got a family christening robe and it's all the more precious to me because both of you had a hand in it."

"And don't you realise, Gran, that without you there wouldn't be a christening!" Sam smiled.

"If you hadn't had Mary, and Mary hadn't had Diane, there wouldn't be any Emma to christen."

"Oh, stop it." Gran's eyes were once again twinkling behind her glasses. "I know I'm not as young as I was, but you make me sound like an old family heirloom myself!"

After everyone had gone, Sam put his arms around Diane and Emma.

"Now," he asked, "how about taking this little heirloom up to bed? She looks quite worn out."

"Mmm, me too." Diane yawned. "It really has been quite a christening!" □

A Mar

He was just another lonely old man.
Then Destiny took a hand . . .

WHEN he'd been young there had been hares on the big field. Pheasants, too, by the score, but now he never even saw the twitch of a mouse's tail.

Things just weren't the same. Nobody understood him any more. Nobody had time to listen.

"Oh, Dad, not that old story," was generally the greeting his tales received.

But it wasn't old to him; it was fresh, and he wanted to keep the memory intact to tell his great-grandchildren when they were old enough.

They would recapture, through his eyes, that moment, long ago, when the first air race had been run from London to Manchester. The planes had flown over, one by one, unwieldy giants that looked as if they were about to fall out of the sky.

He had been a schoolboy then, and the school had been playing cricket on the village green against another school. He could see it as if it were yesterday, the sun shining, the grass greener than grass seemed to be today, the white flannels, and the boys with their bright school caps.

And the slow droning, the incredible sound from the South. They

And His Dog

stopped the game and watched the monsters soar across them.

Across the green the cattle had stampeded and the horses had bolted. The geese ran honking in terror, and the boys all stared. When at last the planes were gone and the sky empty except for a startled bird, even the master had forgotten the score.

Maybe it wasn't the first air race, as Peter said. Peter hadn't been there but he knew everything, read it all out of books, and corrected his father.

"You weren't at Amiens, Dad. You were at Mons."

He ought to know, Ben thought irritably. He'd been a lad then, only 19 and marriage not even dreamed of, let alone four sons to tell him off in his old age and put him right over details only he could know.

He'd been back once, with some of his friends, to Flanders. They had visited the fields of crosses in neat rows under the bright, revealing sun,

Complete Story by JOYCE STRANGER

fields and fields of graves, with the poppies growing. It had been a mistake because it had brought back too many memories.

Memories of Rob and Dave and Ken and Paul, who had never come back and who lay buried under the uncaring sun, while the blood-red petals fell, one by one, and lay like crimson tears.

He had never told his sons about that. They wouldn't have understood — he forgot that they had fought their own war, a war he had been too old for. They had never shared their memories with him.

IT was five years since Mary had died and it was very lonely without her. As he grew older there were fewer people to share his memories with. He found himself talking to someone he thought of as his own generation and finding that they didn't even remember the Second World War, let alone the first.

There were days when he felt older than Time.

He laid the table neatly, the way Mary used to lay it with the starched cloth. His daughters-in-law laughed at him for starching the linen and told him to buy nylon and save himself some work.

Why save work when there was every hour in the day to fill? He had to do something to pass the time.

He would have liked a dog again but the lads said he was too old to care for a dog. He'd find it a nuisance because he would have to take it out, brush it and feed it, shop for it, and maybe even cook for it. It was too much at his age.

He wasn't that old, though he'd never see 70 again, or even 80, though

A MAN AND HIS DOG

he wasn't admitting to that. A man was as young as he felt and Ben didn't feel a day over 65. He was in the prime of life and Dr Bryce had said he was as healthy as any man half his age.

There'd been the day he went out with Fly, the little black dog that had won so many prizes for him. He had mounted the bright rosettes from some of the shows and framed them, to keep the colours free from dust. Nobody could take the record of his achievements away.

He had taken out the old Golden Labrador, what was his name — he could see the dog so plainly, but the name eluded him — and won in the Field Trials. He could do anything with any dog.

Titus, that was the dog's name. Robbie had named him, after someone he was learning about in school. Robbie had funny ideas. He'd named the gaffer's new bull, Toreador Figaro.

He'd been a good gaffer, but he'd died young, much too young, only 78 when he went. No stamina in that family, Ben thought, as he set out his plate, knife and fork, and then served his sausage and mash as if he were serving a king. He always believed you had to keep up your standards or you had nothing left.

He finished his meal, washed the dishes and folded the cloth. He dusted the table although there was no dust on it. There was a wind tonight, and it would be rain before dark. The charged clouds told him more than the weathermen ever did.

Modern ideas were all very well but the old men could show them a thing or two. Ben's old Shires had never had a day off work in their lives and didn't go on strike either.

Ben closed the door behind him, for the cottage was too quiet. He'd walk on the river bank, look at the tumbling water as it thrust over the boulders and see the trees on the hills.

It was quite a long walk but it was time he did something that he wanted to do, instead of always being careful because the boys told him to be. What was he being careful for?

It wasn't the same without Mary.

If he had a dog he could walk every day in the fields and enjoy throwing a stick for it. Or maybe he'd buy it a rubber ring. Titus had loved to pull on his ring. He'd been fun, that dog.

A dog would be company in the night, a creature to talk to. Sometimes he forgot how a human voice sounded, with no-one to talk to for days on end. It wasn't the lads' faults, they were married and busy with their own lives that didn't always include him.

Beyond the coppice the church clock struck seven.

THE dog was alone, wandering forlornly. They had brought him in the car, and opened the door and pushed him out. He had run after the car, crying, because they had forgotten him, but they had accelerated and left him miles from home, in a strange place. He was tired and hungry.

They had walked him on the hills and had fed him, a long time ago. All of them had been strangely quiet, so that he had pawed at them, but they had ignored him. He didn't know that the man had lost his job, and that there was not even enough money to put him down.

If we dump him, they said, maybe someone will find him and give him a life. He was a Golden Labrador and four years old.

He wandered down the path towards the river. He heard the church clock strike but it meant nothing to him. There were no people, anywhere. People meant food.

He wandered on, alone. He had never been alone before. Once he sat and howled at the sky, but nobody was there to hear.

He sniffed aimlessly at trees, and plodded on. They had walked him a long way and he was very tired. He was also very hungry as his only meals for the last two weeks had been household scraps.

He knew nothing of mortgage repayments and hire-purchase repayments and the need for people to feed and be clothed.

At first it had been fun to have his master home all day, but then there were tears and tantrums and angry words, and the dog crept from one place to another to stay unseen.

He had no memory of that. He only knew he was very lonely, and that life had suddenly completely changed and nobody wanted him. He sat and howled again. Somewhere in the distance he heard a faint cry. That meant humans and humans meant food.

His tail began to wave with anticipation and he broke into a run.

Ben had walked farther than he intended to, lured by the evening sun. There was brilliance on the heather and the river was a clear sparkle, and the dark rocks were enticing, asking him to go and sit on one. So he went down the river bank, forgetting the treachery of wet earth, and slipped.

He was safe enough, because he was out of the water, but the bank was narrow and steep and there was nothing to hang on to to help him up.

The dog that appeared above him might have been a reincarnation of Titus. For a moment he thought he was seeing a ghost and then the animal barked at him.

"Here, fellow," he called, and the dog slid down the bank and came to his feet and sat, looking up at him. Ben saw the bleeding pads from the agonised race along the road, a race that went on for miles after the vanishing car.

The dog did not look like a stray. Ben, who had known too much of human callousness, guessed at some of the story.

"You'll have to help me out of here," he said, hoping the dog might climb the bank and pull him up it, but the dog didn't seem to understand.

He was wearing a slip chain, but no collar.

Ben took off his tie and fastened it to the slip chain. He found a stick lying at the edge of the water, and threw it up the bank. No Labrador could ever resist a thrown stick.

A MAN AND HIS DOG

This dog was no exception. His compact muscular body pulled Ben up the bank to safety.

He sat on a tree stump to get his breath and the dog dropped at his feet. Ben removed the tie, and began to walk slowly home with the dog following him.

"All right, fellow, I guess we're meant for each other," Ben said, as he came to his cottage door, and put the key in the lock.

The dog came inside and settled himself on the hearthrug, just as Titus had once done. He watched as Ben went to the cupboard under the sink and brought out the bowl he thought he had put away for-ever, and the big drinking bowl.

TOMORROW he would buy dog food. Tonight they would have to make do. There was a tin of meat in the pantry and plenty of brown bread. Ben filled the bowl and watched the dog eat, then ask to go outside. Ben watched him, a little anxiously. Suppose he went away?

But the dog had come to stay.

"You could be Titus's grandson," Ben told him, "so I'll call you Titus the Second. How do you like your name, Titus, lad?"

The dog sat up and looked at the man who had fed him and taken him in. As Ben dropped into his armchair and turned on the television set, the dog came to him and rested his head on the man's knee.

Ben had never enjoyed his evening's viewing so much. He commented on everything and the dog waved his tail.

At bedtime the dog followed him up the stairs and settled down on the rug. No dog had ever been allowed in Ben's room before, but this dog needed to be wanted. Ben knew now that he had been abandoned.

Anxious eyes followed every move as if pleading with Ben to keep him, and not turn him out on his own. He reached down and patted the dog's head. The warm tongue licking his hand triggered many memories.

Tomorrow he could train this dog as once he'd trained Titus. They'd start a new life together, the two of them. The dog would be a better dog than any dog he'd had before.

Ben wakened early, and found himself looking into two anxious brown eyes. He jumped out of bed with all the vigour of a much younger man, eager to begin the day with his new friend.

The dog bounded downstairs, his tail waving, barking to be let out; he raced in again and barked for food and Ben fed him with a thick slice of brown toast. He needed dog food and dog biscuits and a collar and a lead. He'd been saving all these months to buy himself a treat but he'd never thought of anything that he wanted.

Now he had the money to spend on the dog. He would buy him a bed; and they would walk the moors together and walk beside the river.

The postman was startled when he came up the drive with the letters. Inside the house Ben was whistling and as the man turned away he heard the dog's deep bark.

"I thought it was a ghost I heard," he said that night, telling the story in the Traveller's Rest. "But blow me, when old Ben came to the door, it was just as if he'd been born again. A spring in his step and a laugh in his voice; done him the world of good, that dog has."

All eyes turned to the door, as it opened and old Ben came in. He hadn't been near the place since Mary had died. Earlier, in fact. He'd stopped coming when he lost his last dog.

The Labrador at his side looked serenely round the room and went to lie by the fire.

Ben nodded to everyone, and took his half-pint over to the settle beside his dog.

"Somebody threw him out, I reckon," he said to the watching men. "It's a shame, but it's an ill wind . . . just like my old Titus, born again."

The dog shifted so that he could lie with his head on the old man's foot, and went to sleep, secure in the knowledge that he was wanted. □

LAST RITES

Just one last thing I had to do.
Just one last thing I'd promised you.
With heavy heart and glistening eye
I climbed the hill that met the sky.

No sign of sun, the grey mist swirled,
As it often did in this your world.
I found the place where you would sit
Patiently waiting for the stage to be lit.

Patiently waiting for the curtains to part
Revealing the scene so dear to your heart.
Green fresh meadows, brackens, golden brown,
Snow topped mountains, sleeping market town.

Standing awhile I saw again with you.
Then sadly did what I'd come to do.
Stone cropped fells and the sky above,
No dank dark grave for you my love.

Then, just once, a curlew cried.
No choir boy's treble, it reft the sky.
And I left that place with a lifted heart,
My step much lighter than at the start.

— Mrs L. R., Sunderland.

THE SCHOOL FÊTE WAS A POTENTIAL DISASTER, BUT IT TURNED OUT TO BE MORE SUCCESSFUL THAN ANYONE COULD HAVE IMAGINED!

S OMEBODY once said that if they had to choose between planning a school fête or a state visit, they'd take the state visit any day. Don't ask me who it was. Old Beasley, the headmaster, would probably know. He's the one who's always quoting it. But as he isn't in the habit of divulging sources to his junior sports master, all I can say is that whoever it was, knew what he was talking about.

Mind you, this particular fête wasn't too disorganised once it really got going. We made fifty per cent. more than our target, so if Clare Richards doesn't snaffle the surplus for yet more literary works, I might even manage to get some new gymnasium equipment.

First of all, though, I'll have to deal with the complaints. I haven't had any so far, but should they start coming in, I must admit that the fault was mine and mine alone. There's no-one else to blame.

Although I'll never know why I was co-opted on to their fête committee in the first place.

It was the English department that began the whole thing. Having acquired a new library room, they got greedy and started demanding books to put in it.

Hence the fête, which was to make money for them. And hence my service as one of the organisers.

"It will do you good to get involved in this," Miss Lennie, head of History had said. "Excellent experience for the students."

I didn't argue with Lennie the Lion. Her speciality is the Ancient Romans and believe me she could leave them standing when it comes to demolishing opponents, be they Christian or otherwise.

102

FÊTE LENDS A HAND!

"Well, quite," I said pleasantly, before she could unsheath her claws. "I'd be delighted to help out."

So that was it, and the following Friday at 4.30 p.m., I found myself closeted in the Latin room with my fellow committee members and Clare Richards, whose idea the whole ghastly business had been.

"Do you think it would be too ambitious to have a barbecue at lunch-time?" she suggested. "You know, sausages and jacket potatoes and that sort of thing. We'd get quite a good profit from that."

"Yes, and I could make some of my orange fizz to sell with it," Jimmy Sinclair added. Orange fizz! Whatever next!

"I can just see that going down a bomb," I said. "No, what we want is a few barrels of beer if we're having a barbecue. In fact, if it was up to me —"

"If it were up to you, Mr Wright. Not was up to you," Clare corrected primly.

"And anyway, it's not," she went on. "Up to you, I mean. We're having orange fizz and that's that."

Dreams of a cocktail bar fading, I shut my mouth before I made any more grammatical faux pas.

That's the trouble with English teachers. They won't confine their subject to the classroom. I mean, if I went around expecting her to do handstands all over the place or demonstrate rugby tackles or something, she'd be indignant, wouldn't she?

"Mr Wright! Mr Wright, you're not paying attention."

Miss Lennie had fixed her beady black eye on me, and I resisted the temptation to cower behind a blackboard.

"I was saying," she went on imperiously, "that I suppose the headmaster will be opening the fête, as he usually does on these occasions."

"Actually, I was wondering about that," Clare, a braver character than I, dared to voice some doubt on the matter.

"I was thinking, wouldn't it be rather nice if we could get a celebrity to open it? Someone who'll draw the crowds?"

"I could get Joe Donnelly, the new centre-half with —" I started, but Miss Lennie glared at me and I tailed off.

FÊTE LENDS A HAND!

"Certainly not! I've been reading about that young man. He seems more famous for his activities off the football pitch than on it."

"What about William Dunstable?" Clare suggested. "He lives over at Grangeleigh, and he's certainly well known."

I couldn't argue with that, though admittedly I like him more for his weekly column in the newspaper than for his silly avant-garde plays.

B Y the time I got out of the room, everything was more or less arranged. I had got off quite lightly, I thought later. Organising a five-a-side match for the afternoon was a piece of cake, and keeping in touch with the catering suppliers shouldn't take up too much time.

My only other duty had been to approach William Dunstable about opening the fête, and that had taken only a two-minute phone call. Fortunately he was free on the day, and said he would be delighted to do the honours.

So I relaxed, and thanked my lucky stars that I hadn't been landed with the task of trying to procure half a dozen donkeys.

Or I might have been in the position of Colin Clarke, an old college buddy of mine who got married last year and is now living out at Ashton. When I visited him the Saturday before the fête I found him in a state of deepening despondency.

"It's Marion," he said gloomily. "Or rather, Marion's good works. She's running a bazaar and jumble sale in aid of the local Scout troop, and she's volunteered my services to help out.

"You know that old law that says if something can go wrong, it will go wrong?"

I listened to Colin's long catalogue of disasters, and patted his back.

"You shouldn't take these things to heart, old son," I said breezily.

"Matter of fact, I'm organising a fête myself at the moment." Well, so I was — with a little assistance! "There's nothing to it as long as you keep cool." He gave me a look of disbelief.

"Honestly, there's not," I insisted. "We've even managed to get William Dunstable to come along and open it for us."

"So have we," Colin said smugly, brightening slightly. "In fact, that's about the only thing that has gone right."

We went on to discuss some mutual friends, and that might have been the end of the matter had I not wished him luck with his bazaar as I was leaving.

"When is it, by the way?" I added.

"Saturday," Colin replied. "That is, if we can sort out the row between the mothers who are supplying the food!"

"Saturday?" I stopped at the doorway and frowned back at him. "What time on Saturday?"

"Eleven o'clock. Why?"

"Eleven o'clock? And you think William Dunstable is coming to open it?"

Oh, I hated to do it to him, really I did. The poor guy had enough on his plate without me piling it on.

"Yes, why?" Colin's face took on an anxious expression.

"Look, I think you must have made some mistake," I told him sorrowfully. "You see, William Dunstable is opening our fête, in Malmerton, at eleven o'clock on Saturday."

Colin's expression was a beauty. Have you ever seen someone who's just been told a bulldozer has backed into his brand-new, super de luxe model, ultra-stylish motor car? Well, neither have I, actually, but I imagine he must look something like poor old Colin did then.

"But he can't be," he said eventually. "He wrote to me. He promised he'd come!" His faith was touching!

"Sorry, pal, but I spoke to him on the phone last month, and there's no doubt about it. He's coming to our fête.

"Why don't you ring him up and complain?" I suggested helpfully. "Maybe he'll come along to yours later and say a word or two."

Colin disappeared for a few minutes, then returned. His expression, I noticed, had changed considerably. It was now more like the man who'd been told that, no, it was all a mistake, actually it was his best friend's car the bulldozer had got.

AT NIGHT

Why does Darkness bring security,
When Daylight's careless grin
Welcomes the uncertainty
That the night just won't let in?

Its quilted warmth holds time at bay,
Suppressing the intrusion
Of hands that tick the hours away
To dawn's renewed confusion.

The folds it lays across my eyes
Extend to soothe my mind,
Relaxing me with breath-soft sighs
And whispering "Unwind . . ."

I've always loved this special time,
These hours where troubles cease,
Where solitude and safety rhyme
In a verse of perfect peace.

— *Mrs S. T., Herts.*

"I think it's you who's got the wires crossed," Colin said gleefully. "I've just spoken to him. He says of course he'll be here, and that he's never heard of you or Malmerton High."

FÊTE LENDS A HAND!

"But — but I spoke to him! He can't have!" I snatched the letter Colin was holding and looked down at the heading.

"Here, hold on a minute. That's not the number I called, it was five-five something else. Have you got a phone directory?"

He produced one and I hurriedly scanned the "D"s.

"See, there it is, Dunstable, William, 10 Bank Street. Grangeleigh five-five-two —"

I couldn't keep the grin off my face.

"Pity you hadn't looked further down," Colin said, stabbing a finger at the next reference. "Dunstable, William Barlow Dunstable. That's William Dunstable the playwright. Who do you suppose yours is?"

"The wrong one! What do you mean the wrong one?" Clare Richards asked icily.

"I — er — I looked up William Dunstable in the phone book and when I found one in Grangeleigh I sort of assumed it was him.

"I mean how was I to know that a little place like Grangeleigh would have two William Dunstables? It's not like Smith or something is it?"

"Just who is this William Dunstable?" she demanded.

He didn't know, but Alex Craig the janitor did.

"Willie Dunstable?" he exclaimed. "Oh aye, know him. He used to be a gardener in the Parks Department. He's captain of the Crown and Anchor darts team."

"And — he's coming to — to open our fête — on Saturday," she said slowly.

She was taking it remarkably calmly I thought.

"Yes, well, mistakes do happen," I said consolingly.

"Mistakes!" Clare Richards shouted in outraged tones.

"Mistakes! I bet you did it on purpose you inefficient, incompetent, rugger-playing —" She gulped a few times, her excellent vocabulary for once failing her.

"Oaf?" I suggested, but she didn't seem in the least grateful for any help.

"How on earth can we have a guest of honour no-one's ever heard of except the Crown and Anchor darts team?" Clare asked.

"Er — shouldn't that be, 'of whom no one has ever heard'?" I ventured.

But she paid no attention, the finer points of the English language being unimportant beside the ruination of her great day.

"OK, OK," I said wildly when I could get a word in. "I'll sort it out, I promise. I'll go and see this fellow and tell him it was all a mistake.

"The headmaster can open the fête, and I'll get on to the right William Dunstable and see if he can nip over later for a bit."

I was beginning to envy Colin and his minor problems like moth-eaten marquees and a threatened walk-out by the mothers in charge of catering.

Anything would be preferable to this, I thought, as I knocked on the door of 10 Bank Street.

"Mr Dunstable?" I enquired, extending a hand. "I'm Tom Wright, from

106

Malmerton High. I phoned you about the fête."

A little gnome-like man with the beginnings of a beard grinned up at me and waved me indoors.

"You'll have a cup of tea," he told me, after I'd been settled in the best chair.

"Yes, I think perhaps I'd better," I began, taking a deep breath. "I expect you're wondering —"

"Milk and sugar, Mr Wright? Oh, I'm fair excited about Saturday," he raced on. "Mind you, I can't think why you want me to open your fête."

"Yes, ah, that's what I —"

"Anything to oblige, that's what my missus always used to say when she was alive. I was telling my daughter about it when I wrote last week."

He put a cup down on the table at my side. "She's in Australia now, of course, but she went to the High herself, and she'll be tickled to know about her old dad."

I sipped my tea in silence while William Dunstable, retired gardener, chattered on.

"Now," he said finally, sitting down opposite me, "what else was it you wanted to see me about?"

"I — er —" I floundered. "I just wanted to — to check that everything was all right for Saturday."

AND everything was all right for Saturday. The sun shone, the barbecue sizzled nicely, and even old Sinclair's orange fizzy sold out. The donkeys behaved admirably, and class 3C managed to act like human beings instead of the malevolent, marauding little fiends they undoubtedly are.

In fact, the only fly in the ointment might have been Clare Richards, but I spent the day avoiding her.

It was nearly four o'clock before she caught up with me. As I was trapped at the coconut shy with Miss Lennie on one side and a barrage of balls on the other, there wasn't much I could do when I saw her striding purposefully over the grass.

"There you are," she said accusingly. "I've been looking everywhere for you!"

I looked round frantically for another way of escape. "I'm sorry. I know I told you I would fix it all, but old Willie was —"

"— absolutely brilliant," Clare exclaimed. "I've never heard a speech like it."

I stared at her.

"He was marvellous," Clare repeated. "That story he told about the plants that were being eaten away, and how he stood guard with a shotgun all night, thinking it was rabbits, and discovered the culprit was a caterpillar!

"I haven't laughed so much in ages. He's a natural-born storyteller!"

"He is? I mean, he is," I hurriedly agreed.

"And let's face it," she went on, "anyone can have a celebrity to open a

FÊTE LENDS A HAND!

fête these days. The other William Dunstable is OK, but he could never have touched people's hearts the way yours did. He was a stroke of genius."

I tried to appear suitably modest as I smiled at her. And you know something? She really was something to look at. In a light sundress with strappy shoulders, Miss Richards of the English department looked positively feminine, would you believe!

"You know, you're really quite a decent sort in spite of the act you put on, aren't you?" Clare mused.

"Who is?" I asked indignantly.

"You are," Clare insisted. "You knew opening this fête was the biggest thing that has happened to Willie Dunstable for years and you couldn't disappoint him."

She smiled a really attractive smile.

"Look at him, over there, telling Mr Beasley a joke."

Clare waved, and Willie disentangled himself from the Head and came towards us.

It was a different Willie than the one I had seen earlier in the week. Gone was the three-week stubble and worn cardigan. Willie's thinning hair was neatly combed and he sported his best suit.

"Seems to have gone well, eh, Tom?" he said.

"After the start you gave, are you surprised?" I asked, and he shook his head wonderingly.

"I'll never understand why you wanted me to do this," he went on. "Of course, I've always been a bit of a story-teller and word gets round, I suppose.

"But to be guest of honour, me . . ." He tailed off, his eyes searching the crowd.

"Oh, excuse me a minute, will you?" he said after a moment. "I've just spotted Euphemia and I promised to give her some tips on geraniums."

"Euphemia?" I said questioningly to Clare.

She shrugged.

"Probably one of the — no, I don't believe it!"

"Euphemia Lennie," I choked as I watched the Lion go off arm in arm with Willie.

"Yes, you've definitely got your better side, Tom Wright," Clare said when she stopped laughing. "I think you've made an old man very happy."

I hesitated for a moment and then decided to jump in at the deep end.

"Um, how'd you like to make a young man very happy?" I enquired. "Have dinner with me tonight?"

Later, as I got ready to meet her, I had some doubts about the wisdom of my suggestion. After all, an English lesson over dinner isn't my idea of a perfect evening.

On the other hand, though, I thought as I knotted my tie, if Miss Richards reverted to classroom tactics I could always order her to do a cartwheel around the table! □

It's not easy for a young girl to convince her mother she's being selfish — especially when she spends every spare moment helping others.

Young Tessa's Dilemma

Complete Story by DI HARDIE

I WAS worried about Mrs Marston from the moment she moved into my house. She had a nice room overlooking the street, and I'd made it as comfortable as I could, with a big armchair, little cooking stove, good warm fire, and all the other things I felt she would need.

But she was old, and she always seemed to be alone. I had more than enough to keep me busy, with three children, a home, and a full-time job. And Mrs Marston never made any attempt to bother me.

She kept strictly to her room. From the time I came hurrying in from work in the evening to the moment when I slammed the front door behind me in the morning, sending the children off to school before I ran to the bus stop, I rarely saw her.

But she was there, all alone, and it bothered me. Several times, I offered her a break from the loneliness. I was always busy, but I thought she might like to sit with the children for a while and watch television. Once I invited her to have tea with us.

Yet each time she refused — politely, but with a prim, decisive firmness that left no room for doubt.

I told myself she didn't want her privacy invaded; she wanted to be alone.

But it wasn't easy to put her completely out of my mind. I wasn't even

109

YOUNG TESSA'S DILEMMA

sure where my duty to her began and ended, as I'd never had a lodger before.

But I needed Mrs Marston now. She was part of my resolution not to fail Jim.

When Jim, my husband, had died, I'd cried until it seemed there was no end to the tears.

With him there had been everything, and without him suddenly there seemed to be nothing. Nothing except three grief-stricken children, a house wrapped in the sudden hush of misery, and endless tears.

Friends and neighbours had done their best. They'd helped with the funeral, and tried to comfort the children. Then they'd gone back to their own lives.

Then, one day, four-year-old Carol had come to me as I sat hunched in an armchair, still shaking with sobs.

One small hand had slid into mine and her soft lips had brushed my wet cheek.

"Mummy," she'd said gently, "I want some clean socks."

"Not now, darling." I hadn't lifted my head. I had whispered. "Not now."

"But, Mummy . . ." Gently but firmly, her small hands had circled my face. She'd turned my head so that I was looking into her eyes. Her little face had been pale but serious.

"But, Mummy," she'd said quietly. "I must have clean socks."

I had stared at her for a long time, then put out my arms and pulled her to me.

She had nestled close, and the tears had slowly dried on my cheeks.

I don't mean that in that moment I found an instant answer to my problems. It wasn't as easy as that.

It was just that I had known she was right. She did have to have clean socks, and eight-year-old Malcolm had to be reminded to feed his pet rabbit, and 10-year-old Tessa had to be taken to the dentist for a filling.

Life had to go on. Children had to be cared for. And from now on, there was only me to do it.

I HADN'T cried any more. Not in front of the children anyway. Alone, on the hearthrug in front of the fire, with Jim's photograph in my hand, I had tried to take a clear, honest look at things. Jim was gone. All the tears and all the sadness couldn't bring him back, and with him had gone a world of dreams.

But not all of them. There were still the dreams we had fashioned for the children, the plans we had made for them, the good, happy life Jim had wanted for us all. That needn't die. It was up to me to try to make it work.

I'd still been sad and confused, but suddenly I had a purpose. It seemed to comfort me and give me strength.

More than anything, I hadn't wanted to give up the house. It wasn't big or particularly special, but Jim and I had been happy in it.

110

It was full of memories of him, and they seemed to surround me, giving me a sense of reassurance. I had felt the children needed that, too.

But money was a problem. I'd been only 18 when Tessa was born, and I hadn't worked since.

I was lucky. I got a job in a little shop just off the High Street.

The owner was kind, and allowed me to finish in time to pick up Carol from nursery school, provided I kept my lunch hour to a minimum.

With her clinging to my hand, I would double back to the supermarket, pick up what I needed for the evening meal, then head hastily for home.

By the time Tessa and Malcolm came in from school, I had switched on the lights, lit the fire, put on the kettle, and tied on my apron.

It wasn't easy. Sometimes I had to stand for a few minutes alone in the kitchen to get my breath back, but it was important for the house to be warm and bright and welcoming, the same as it had always been.

Money was still my problem. I had budgeted as carefully as I could, but there was always still a gap.

I could work as hard as I liked, run as fast as I could, and spend every evening and every weekend washing and ironing and making and mending, but it still wasn't going to work.

It was then I thought of taking in a lodger.

At first, I couldn't quite come to terms with the idea of a stranger in our home, but eventually practicality took over.

The upstairs front bedroom, the one Jim and I had shared, would be most suitable. Tessa and Carol already shared a room, so they wouldn't have to be disturbed at all.

Malcolm would be only too delighted to hand over his little room to me, and move up to the attic once it had been cleared and decorated.

Having come to my decision, I talked to the children.

"It won't make much difference to us," I wanted to reassure them. "Whoever it is that comes to live here, we'll just have to be polite and considerate to them. Other than that, our lives will go on just the same."

I'm not sure what I expected their reactions to be. If there was to be a problem, I suppose I presumed it would come from Malcolm — there were times when he could show resentment against anything new.

Or, if not Malcolm, then perhaps Carol. She was only four, and shy of anyone unknown.

But neither Malcolm nor Carol showed any great reaction. It was Tessa who suddenly stood up and walked towards the door.

"Tessa!" I was surprised. "Where are you going?"

She hesitated. "Upstairs."

"But . . . I was trying to explain to you about letting a room to help, now that . . ."

She stared at me, flatly.

"I don't care what you do." Then she went out, closing the door sharply behind her.

I was amazed. Tessa had always been the easiest one of the three to understand.

YOUNG TESSA'S DILEMMA

Tessa never flew into a temper, Tessa was the reliable one. You always knew where you were with Tessa.

Thinking it over later, I felt I understood.

Perhaps, being older, she was more vulnerable. Perhaps she saw a lodger as someone who would eat up even more of my precious time. Suddenly, I started to think.

Caught up in my new life, I hadn't been concentrating on the children. I had been doing everything practical for them, but I hadn't been conscious of their other, more important needs.

I began to be. Malcolm and Carol, I noticed, seemed to have grown more loving, more dependent, since Jim's death.

Carol threw her arms round my neck at the slightest pretext and Malcolm had taken to giving me a passing hug, sometimes even a quick kiss, when he came in from school.

But not Tessa. She rarely came wandering into the kitchen to find me, or hovered round me like the other two did, and never impulsively hugged or kissed me. Much of the time, she would shut herself away in her room with a book.

She was good and she was obedient, but it was almost as though she had drawn away from me.

I was worried. I could see no alternative to taking in a lodger, but I decided to make an extra effort where Tessa was concerned.

I ADVERTISED the following week, as soon as the room was ready. Mrs Marston came that evening. She sat primly on the edge of an armchair, clasping her little handbag tightly in her lap. She was a widow, she explained. Now that her husband was dead, she could no longer afford the flat they'd lived in and my room would suit her very well.

She seemed ideal.

So she moved in the following Saturday. Malcolm and Carol stood in the hall, watching, as I helped carry one of her suitcases upstairs.

They returned her polite smile with stiff uncertainty. But Tessa was missing, and I knew instinctively she would be in her room reading.

Over tea that evening, I cheerfully broached the subject of Mrs Marston.

"She's old, so we must be very thoughtful, and not make too much noise at times when she's probably asleep, and that sort of thing.

"And, of course, we mustn't intrude on her — no-one is to go into her room unless they're invited. But she seems a very lonely person, so if she speaks to you, do stop and have a little chat with her."

But Mrs Marston made no attempt to chat to the children or to me. She wasn't unfriendly — she smiled if we caught sight of each other, and she even, very occasionally, commented on the weather. It was just a brief sentence or two, though, then she quietly went back to the solitude of her room.

I didn't like to think of her all alone all the time.

She had no television, just a radio. I thought she might like to watch a programme now and then with the children, but she refused.

"Oh, no." She had a swift, crisp way of speaking. "Thank you very much, but no."

It was the same when I offered to bring anything she needed from the supermarket, and the same again the day it was raining hard and I offered to pop her washing through the spin-drier.

And it was the same when I invited her to have tea with us.

"Oh, no. Thank you very much, but no."

I wasn't exactly hurt, but I gave up. I felt there was nothing more I could do.

"She's an old lady, and I think she just wants to be by herself," I told the children. "We must just be polite to her and not intrude."

"But why didn't she come to tea?" Carol couldn't understand. "Did you tell her we had jelly and fruit for afters?"

Malcolm shook his head, obviously not really understanding either. "Perhaps she doesn't like fruit and jelly," he suggested.

Tessa said nothing.

She seemed to have become more and more silent. When I talked to her now, she answered, but there was none of the old happy animation.

I thought sometimes that she was paler and thinner, but usually I convinced myself that I was imagining it. I was doing all I could to make her happy.

She had a school friend, Anna, who lived across the road. Tessa had taken to spending a lot of time playing at her house, and I was glad, if it made her laugh occasionally.

IT was Anna who mentioned Sandra's party. Sandra lived in a big house, Anna told me, her father had a big car, and her mother was arranging an absolutely super birthday party for her.

Everyone in the class was going, and she, Anna, was having a new dress specially for the occasion.

The party was only a few days away, and I couldn't understand why Tessa hadn't mentioned it. When I asked her, she simply shrugged.

"I was going to, but you were busy," she said flatly. "You're always doing things."

For a moment, I felt unreasonably hurt. But she was only ten years old, and very unhappy.

Alone that evening, I thought about it. I loved her, and more than anything I didn't want to fail her. She would go to the party, and, if possible, she would go in a new dress.

In my lunch hour next day, I ran from shop to shop. There were innumerable pretty dresses, but the prices were all impossible.

I thought about it the rest of the day. There seemed only one answer, but it wasn't an easy one.

I had let down hems, shortened sleeves, and stitched in extra pockets. But I had never made a dress — a special party dress to make a sad little girl happy.

H

YOUNG TESSA'S DILEMMA

During my next lunch-time, I bought a paper pattern and some pretty rose-pink material.

After tea, I showed Tessa the material. She ran her fingers over it, and a sense of relief filled me.

She stared at me.

"Can I stay up while you make it?"

I wished she hadn't asked. I was already tired and edgy and it was going to be a long, trying session.

I hugged her.

"No, love. You go to bed. I've got a lot of other things to do first. But don't you worry — it'll be done in time. I promise it will."

She went without another word.

I worked till three in the morning. I made mistakes, with being nervous and clumsy. And, when I was too tired to go on, I found I'd cut out two fronts and had no material left to cut the back.

The next day I bought some more material and some pretty braid. I was still determined the dress should be beautiful.

I worked till two the next morning. My eyes were aching, and so was my head. But the pieces of pink had begun to fit together.

When I crept upstairs I could hear Mrs Marston coughing, and Tessa was tossing restlessly. But I was content.

I had one more night, and I was sure the dress would be ready.

But the next evening, there were so many other things happening. Malcolm had fallen at football. His shorts were torn and covered in mud, and he needed them again the following morning.

Carol's tummy was upset. It took a lot of cuddling to get her to sleep.

I knew Tessa was anxious, and I knew she wondered whether the dress would be finished in time. But she said nothing — just quietly kissed me goodnight and went off to her bed.

I was determined; and I did, finally, finish it.

It was almost four o'clock when the last frill was gathered into place, and the hem was turned up. Then I carefully pressed it.

I hung it up in the living-room so that Tessa could see it when she came down to breakfast.

I watched her face when she did, and her relief was obvious — and rewarding.

"Thank you, Mum," she said, quietly.

But Carol danced with delight.

"It's so pretty," she said. "Can I have a dress like that, Mummy?"

I hastily caught her hand and pulled her away.

"I was only trying to touch it. It looks all nice and soft." She was delighted.

I made silly mistakes that day. I was too tired, and it made me edgy. The one thing I couldn't afford was to lose my job.

I ran all the way to pick up Carol that afternoon, then all the way to the supermarket. I wanted to be sure Tessa wasn't late for her party.

When I got home, I quickly dumped Carol in front of the television set and rushed into the kitchen to prepare tea.

I heard Tessa and Malcolm come in. After a moment Malcolm came into the kitchen and gave me a rough hug.

"We won today at football," he said. "I'm getting better. Reckon I'll be in the team all right!"

"Good." I pulled away from him. The chops were sizzling and I hadn't finished peeling the potatoes.

"Tell Tessa I'll be as quick as I can with tea," I said. "It'd probably be best if she goes straight up and has a good wash and brushes her hair, then . . ."

THE cry from the living-room was loud and unexpected. I jumped and the knife slipped, and blood spurted red from my finger. I snatched up a tea-cloth, wound it round my hand, and darted into the living-room.

Tessa was staring in dismay at the dress, which was on the floor. It was a crumpled pink heap, half spread across the carpet, half screwed down behind an armchair.

"Carol! You did that, didn't you?" Malcolm was angry. "After all Mum's work!"

"I didn't! I didn't! I didn't!" Carol's small face was flushed with guilt.

"You did so. I saw you. You were jumping up and down trying to touch it. Now Mum's got to iron it all over again."

"I didn't! I didn't! I didn't!"

Carol's shrill squeal echoed through my head, the cut on my finger throbbed, and the blood stained the tea-cloth.

Something inside me seemed to collapse and tears filled my eyes. I fled up the stairs into my little bedroom and closed the door.

I sat on the edge of my bed, just holding my finger, for a long time. Until the bleeding — and the tears — had almost stopped. I felt exhausted, and guilty.

I barely heard the tap at the door. Tessa came in, very carefully balancing a tray. On it was a packet of adhesive plasters and a cup of tea.

"You should drink it while it's hot, Mrs Marston said." She held out the cup and saucer.

"Mrs Marston?" I stared at her.

Tessa nodded.

"First she made some tea, and now she's ironing my dress."

"But how . . .?" I broke off. I could hardly believe it.

Tessa stared at me.

"I asked her to," she said almost defiantly. "I told her you were tired, and you'd cut your finger."

"But, darling . . ." Guilt swamped me again. The old lady had wanted so much to be left alone. "You shouldn't have . . ."

"Why not?" Suddenly Tessa's big brown eyes were angry. "She didn't mind. She was glad to help."

Impatiently she swung away from me and headed quickly for the door, but then she hesitated, her face rather pale.

"Don't you understand? She didn't want you doing things for her. Always busy, then trying to find time to be kind to her as well. That's not what she wanted."

Her lips quivered slightly.

"That doesn't make people feel happy. It just makes them feel a nuisance."

She had flung open the door and was halfway down the stairs before I called her back.

She came slowly, reluctantly, and stood in the doorway. I had tried so hard yet missed so much.

I put out my hand and hesitantly she came to me. I patted the bed and she sat down beside me, staring at the floor.

"I'm sorry," she began miserably.

But I shook my head.

"Tessa." I caught at the first words that came. "You're right. I am tired; too tired."

I didn't glance at her but I knew she had turned her head and was looking at me.

"I've tried to do everything, but I can't. Not by myself, I need some help."

For a moment she didn't say anything, then she took a plaster from the packet. Carefully, she put it on my cut finger.

"I could help you," she said slowly. "If you'd let me. I could make my bed and Carol's in the morning, and help Malcolm with his." Her voice quickened.

"And I could do the shopping. Anna does nearly all her mother's. And she dusts and vacuums the carpets, and . . ."

"Can I come in?" Carol appeared in the doorway. She hesitated, then sidled up to me and put her arms tightly round my neck.

"Mrs Marston said Tessa's dress is ready. And she's finished the potatoes. And would you like her to put them on to cook?"

She planted an apologetic kiss on my cheek. "I did knock the dress down, and I'm sorry."

"Oh, Carol, darling," I began.

But Tessa took her gently but firmly by the hand. "You come with me, Titch," she said. "Let Mum rest a big longer. She can come down when tea's ready. Mrs Marston and I can manage."

She paused at the door as Carol went scampering ahead of her down the stairs.

"Is it all right for me to go to the party?"

"Of course," I answered.

"Thank you, Mum. And when I come home the others will be in bed. Perhaps we could talk, just us?"

"Over a nice hot cup of chocolate." I smiled.

She smiled back at me, brightly, happily, eagerly. And, suddenly, we were wonderfully close again. □

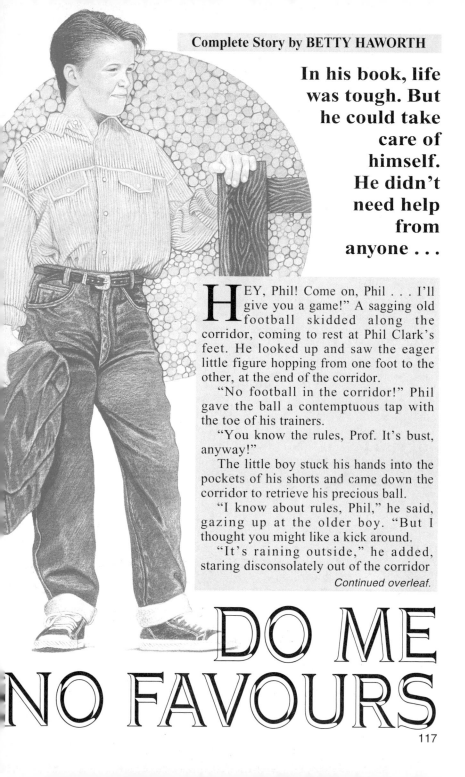

Complete Story by BETTY HAWORTH

In his book, life was tough. But he could take care of himself. He didn't need help from anyone . . .

HEY, Phil! Come on, Phil . . . I'll give you a game!" A sagging old football skidded along the corridor, coming to rest at Phil Clark's feet. He looked up and saw the eager little figure hopping from one foot to the other, at the end of the corridor.

"No football in the corridor!" Phil gave the ball a contemptuous tap with the toe of his trainers.

"You know the rules, Prof. It's bust, anyway!"

The little boy stuck his hands into the pockets of his shorts and came down the corridor to retrieve his precious ball.

"I know about rules, Phil," he said, gazing up at the older boy. "But I thought you might like a kick around.

"It's raining outside," he added, staring disconsolately out of the corridor

Continued overleaf.

DO ME NO FAVOURS

117

DO ME NO FAVOURS

Continued from previous page.

window. "And Matron says I've not to go out for any reason what . . . so . . . ever!"

He grinned at Phil, and grimaced. "Fuss, fuss, fuss!"

Phil looked down at the pinched little face. He didn't really know what was wrong with the Prof. except that he was too small for his 10 years and spent too much time in the sick-room of the children's home.

Prof. had been at Greenways ever since he was a baby. He had become a sort of mascot with his funny little face behind the huge spectacles.

Somehow, rules tended to get bent a little where Prof. was concerned. Nobody said much when his plate came back with most of his dinner untouched, or when he was caught reading under the bedclothes with a torch, or when he kicked his old football up and down the corridor.

There were times when Phil was almost envious of Prof.

Not because he was allowed these small favours, for they were only allowed because Prof. was so little and so often poorly. Who wanted favours, anyway? And not because everyone at Greenways was fond of Prof. — who cared about that?

It was because Prof. seemed to accept life so placidly. He accepted that he'd never known his parents, never had a proper home, never known what it was like to have ordinary good health — all the things that most people had as their right.

What you never have, you never miss, Phil thought bitterly, looking at Prof. hugging his battered old ball.

In his blackest moments, Phil always came round to thinking about Prof. He couldn't care less about any of the other people at Greenways, but he sometimes wondered, desperately, what would become of Prof.

When he grew up, Prof. would have to leave the only home he'd ever known and venture out into the cold hostility of the outside world. He didn't know anything about what was waiting outside — the kicks and the disappointments and the unfairness. He still had that to come, on top of everything else.

"You'll get in trouble if Mr Harris catches you," Phil said now.

"He's gone out," Prof. told him confidentially. "In the car, to a meeting. And Miss Parsons is in the office — I heard her answer the phone just now."

"Quite the detective, aren't we?" Phil said, sarcastically. "Well, I haven't time to mess about with you, Miss Parsons wants these books."

Prof. bit his lip and turned away, "OK, Phil."

He looked up at the bigger boy. "I saw the footy team on the noticeboard this morning, and your name isn't on."

"So what?" Phil said. "Who wants to be in the stupid football team? I've got better things to do on a Saturday afternoon."

"Why don't you play in the team?" Prof. asked, puzzled. "They keep asking you — why don't you?"

"Because he thinks he's too good!"

Both boys turned. Maureen Sullivan was coming along from Matron's

118

room. Maureen was tall and slim, just a bit older than Phil and with a mop
of unruly red hair. She smiled at the Prof. and tossed her head at Phil.

"Nobody asked your opinion, Carrots!" Phil retorted, but Maureen
sailed on, with her tilted nose in the air.

"Don't know why they keep asking," she threw over her shoulder.
"Don't know why anybody bothers with you, Phil Clark!"

"She likes you, Phil," Prof. said judiciously. "She really likes you. I
can tell!"

"She's a menace."

"I know she's bossy," Prof. said. "But last time I was ill she was ever
so kind. She read to me for ages and showed me how to fold paper and
make things. It's called . . . ori . . . origanally . . ."

Phil was going to laugh until he looked at Prof. He was very pale and
had sat down against the corridor wall with his football on his lap. Phil
knew he should ask if he was all right or take him to Matron.

But he couldn't stand anybody who was ill, so he turned and went into
Miss Parson's office with the books she wanted.

YVONNE PARSONS looked up and smiled. "Thanks, Phil. How are
things?" "All right," he answered curtly. He stood just inside the
office door, with the familiar guarded look on his young face.

"Mrs Hall rang up just now," Yvonne told him. "She wants to know if
you'd like to go and have tea with them again on Saturday?" She watched
him.

Phil didn't answer right away. He stared down at his shoes, then out of
the office window.

Yvonne sighed inwardly, wishing she knew what he was thinking.

"OK. If you like."

"It's not what I like, Phil," Yvonne said, patiently. "Do you want to go
to the Halls' or not? You enjoyed it last time, didn't you?"

"It was all right."

Yvonne got up irritably and took the books from him. He was very
careful that their hands shouldn't touch. Then he went and stood by the
door.

"Mr and Mrs Hall have been good friends to us at Greenways," she
said. "They're kind people and they love children."

"But they haven't any of their own," Phil interrupted, and she stopped
and stared at him.

"What's that got to do with it?"

"P'raps if they had, they wouldn't be quite so keen."

His hands were thrust into the pockets of his jeans in an attempt to
look nonchalant, but she saw the resentful bitterness in his eyes and her
heart ached for him.

Phil Clark was a handsome boy, or would be if he threw off the studied
insolence and the "who cares" attitude. They had no behaviour problems
with Phil like they did with some of the other older boys, simply because
Phil spent most of his time on his own and spoke as little as possible.

DO ME NO FAVOURS

If he fought sometimes or broke the occasional window, they would know how to deal with him!

"No, Phil," Yvonne said casually. "Mr and Mrs Hall haven't any children of their own, but they like having children from Greenways in their home."

"I bet they do!"

Yvonne was amazed at the bitterness in his young voice. He saw her surprise and burst out suddenly in a way she'd never heard him do before.

"There's a lot of people like that about, aren't there? People who enjoy doing good deeds?" His voice heavy with sarcasm, and his face set hard.

"Yes, Phil. The world would be a poor sort of place without people like that. Kindness costs nothing."

He took a step towards the desk.

"They don't do their good deeds out of kindness," he said.

"They do them because it makes them feel good. Other people find out and everybody says, 'Aren't they good? Aren't they kind?'

"And it's really nothing but a lot of show. It makes me sick."

Yvonne stared at him aghast. His face was white and his hands clenched and she was almost afraid, he was so angry. She knew he was going to storm out and she broke in quickly.

"I'm sorry you feel like that, Phil. I think you're wrong — especially about the Halls."

But his outburst had turned into sullen silence.

"I'd like you to go and see Mr and Mrs Hall on Saturday," Yvonne told him. "They'd be so pleased. Will you?"

"I suppose so," he replied sullenly.

She picked up her pen with a gesture of dismissal.

"I wish everybody would leave me alone," he said from the door, and she glanced up. "I mean it," he said loudly. "I wish people would stop interfering and leave me alone!"

"You've got a lot to learn, Phil," Yvonne said curtly. "Nobody can get through life without help from others. We all have to rely on each other."

"Not me!" he said with determination. "When I leave here, I'm not going to rely on anybody, it doesn't work! I'll manage my own life without any favours, thanks!"

He went out and a moment later Mr Harris came in and closed the door.

"Trouble?"

Yvonne shook her head in exasperation. "Why is he so bitterly resentful of anyone who tries to help him?"

Mr Harris smiled at her, but his kindly face was tired. "It's understandable, Yvonne," he said. "And inevitable perhaps. He's been brought up on favours and now he's reached the age when he knows it.

"All youngsters of Phil's age are vulnerable and insecure, but a boy with his background has even more problems to cope with."

"He's not the only one," Yvonne pointed out reasonably. "Greenways is full of children with problems."

"Phil is rather exceptional," Mr Harris said, his brows drawn together. "He's an intelligent boy, and a highly sensitive one. He's trying to deny that sensitivity because he's been hurt once and he's afraid of letting down all his careful defences again.

"He had what he thought was a secure home until he was six years old — then, suddenly, it was all gone. How do you expect a six-year-old child to understand that his father's got fed-up and walked out and his mother's too emotionally disturbed to be responsible any more?"

He turned and stared out of the window, his thoughtful face set in grim lines.

"A child of six can't understand, but a young man of sixteen understands only too well. It's going to take him a long time to come to terms — if he ever does."

MRS HALL had made one of her splendid high teas. Phil ate heartily but didn't say very much. After tea, Mr Hall suggested that he and Phil go to the evening match.

At the turnstile Phil pushed forward and put his money down before Mr Hall could pay, causing a feeling of awkwardness that spoilt the evening.

Mr Hall made no comment but after the match, when they left the ground with the crowds, he said, "I won't ask you to come back home for supper, Phil. I expect you want to get back now."

Phil heard the note of disappointment in his usually cheery voice but answered carefully.

"OK. There's a programme I want to watch on TV."

They drove back to Greenways through a slow drizzle of rain, and Phil stared moodily out of the window at the wet streets and traffic. When they were on the quieter road to the children's home, Mr Hall spoke, his voice sounding forced.

"Thought what you're going to do when you leave school, Phil?"

"Not yet."

"Things a bit difficult at the moment," Mr Hall said. "But don't get disheartened if you don't find a job right away. Something will turn up."

"I'll manage, thanks," Phil said. "I've got contacts."

If Mr Hall had been less wise he might have laughed.

"Tell you what," he said cheerfully. "I could do with a bit of help at weekends, at the market. What about coming down on Saturday mornings to give me a hand? You've got some likely-looking muscles, and —"

"I'm usually busy on Saturdays," Phil's voice was curt.

They had reached a crossroads and Phil put on his baseball cap firmly.

"You can drop me here," he said, and Mr Hall drew into the side of the road without a word and leant across to open the door.

"All right, Phil. Let me know if you change your mind."

Phil got out, slammed the car door and ran through the rain without glancing back. As he reached the gates of Greenways, an ambulance emerged from the drive and turned right towards town.

DO ME NO FAVOURS

Phil stood watching its bright blue light through the rainy darkness. As it approached the traffic lights, the siren began to wail and seconds later it had disappeared into the traffic.

Phil began to run along the drive, a sudden tight fear in his chest. He could see the main door standing open, and lights on in the hall and the downstairs rooms. As he reached the front steps he saw Mr Harris's car parked, and Maureen Sullivan standing on the steps.

"What's up?"

She gave him a cold look.

"Nothing that would interest you."

But he seized her arm. "I asked you a question . . . what's happened?" he asked again.

Maureen looked in astonishment at the hand on her arm, then at Phil's angry face. Tears filled her eyes and began running down her face.

"It's Prof. They've taken him to hospital!" She wiped her eyes roughly on the sleeve of her cardigan.

"It was awful! Mr Harris picked him up and Prof. said, 'I want my football, it's gone on the roof' and then he went an awful colour, and . . ." She gave a sob.

Miss Parsons was coming downstairs with a suitcase, her face anxious.

"I'm going to the hospital in Mr Harris's car, Maureen," she said hurriedly. "He's gone in the ambulance, and I'll ring as soon as I know what's happening."

She ran out into the rain and got into the car. As she started the engine, the passenger door opened and Phil got in without a word.

T HE HOSPITAL was busy. A clerk at the reception desk directed them up to the children's ward, where they found Mr Harris pacing up and down outside.

"They're getting him ready for theatre, but I don't know any more than that. Sister wants us in her office."

Phil went to the door of the ward and looked in cautiously. He hated the smell of hospitals and wished he hadn't come — but somehow he hadn't really thought what he was doing until now.

Halfway down the ward was a bed with the curtains drawn round it. It was quiet and the overhead lights were turned off, leaving the big ward dimly lit. Phil realised that it must be quite late.

As he stood, hesitantly, a nurse came out from behind the curtains with a trolley and wheeled it away, disappearing through another door. He looked around quickly but Mr Harris and Miss Parsons had gone into the Sister's office, and there was no-one about.

Phil slipped softly through the ward door. His trainers made no sound on the polished floor.

When he reached the curtained bed he stood looking at Prof.

A shaded light was on above the bed and Prof. was lying with his eyes closed. He looked very small and lost and painfully thin.

Phil looked at him for a long time. He hadn't seen Prof. without his big spectacles before — he looked odd. Truth to tell, Phil had never really looked at Prof. properly before today.

A slow pain filled his chest as he saw how frail the little boy was, and he thought that perhaps Prof. might be going to die.

He was going to have an operation. How could such a very small, frail body stand up to such an ordeal? He hadn't any strength in him at all. If he did get through an operation he would have to fight to get better afterwards.

Was there any point in all this?

Prof. seemed to have missed out all along the line . . . no fun, no real home, no parents, nobody at all except Mr Harris and Miss Parsons and the other people at Greenways, and none of them really counted.

Prof. didn't belong to them.

Then he noticed that Prof. was watching him, a little lopsided grin appearing.

"Hiya, Phil!"

"Hello, Prof.," Phil said. "You, OK?"

"OK, Phil," Prof. said. "Tired."

He closed his eyes again, and Phil leaned over him anxiously.

"I'll have to go, Prof.," he whispered. "I don't think I should be in here, really." He turned away but Prof. lifted his arm.

"Don't go, Phil," he said. "I'm scared."

Without thinking, Phil took Prof.'s hand and held it tight in his own.

"You'll be OK, Prof.," he said fiercely. "Don't worry."

"Do me a favour, Phil?"

Prof. was sliding into sleep, his hand in Phil's starting to slacken its grip.

"OK, Prof."

"Don't go, Phil. I want you to be here when . . . I wake up again. Will you, Phil? Please?"

"All right."

"Promise, Phil?"

"Promise, Prof. Go to sleep."

Slowly, the little boy slid into unconsciousness. Phil released his hand and stood up. He went back down the ward and found Mr Harris and Miss Parsons with Sister.

"He's gone to sleep," he said. "I'm staying until . . . after."

Miss Parsons opened her mouth to say something and stopped, looking at Mr Harris. There was a pause then Sister spoke.

"It might be quite a while . . ."

"It doesn't matter," Phil said. "I promised."

"Right," she said. "I suggest you go and get a cup of tea, then you want to wait in the visitors' room at the end of the corridor."

Phil walked away, and Miss Parsons ran after him.

"Don't worry, Phil. Sister says they've found out what's wrong at last, and he's going to be better than he's ever been before."

Phil nodded, then went downstairs to the hospital cafe.

DO ME NO FAVOURS

He was tired and his legs shook as if he'd been running hard. When he had drunk a cup of strong, sweet tea he felt better. Prof. was going to be all right, he felt sure of that now. He thought of when Prof. would be well enough to leave hospital and to return to Greenways. Then everybody would be fussing round trying to show each other how kind they were, trying to outdo each other with good deeds.

B
UT somehow, the thought didn't make Phil angry any more, because he didn't care a bit about anybody else. He was the one who was there when Prof. needed reassuring, and he was the one Prof. had asked to stay — not Mr Harris or Miss Parsons or anybody else.

Nobody had ever asked him to do something like that before — they had all been too busy showing him how sorry they were for him, and trying to interfere in his life.

Perhaps Miss Parsons was right when she said people needed to rely on each other. Prof. certainly needed someone, poor little kid, and it was Phil Clark that he wanted . . . that he really relied on!

Phil finished his tea and walked back to the entrance to the wards. It would be great when Prof. was better!

He'd make sure that people didn't smother him with sympathy. Then, when he was fit again, there would be football . . . Prof.'s beloved football, that he'd never been able to play properly before — not in a real team, in a real game, with a decent ball . . .

There was a telephone near the entrance to the wards. Phil stood and looked at it for a minute, then fished in his pocket and found some coins.

The phone rang and rang and he wanted to hang up, but he made himself wait. Mr Hall's voice was cheerful when he answered and Phil took a deep breath.

"Mr Hall? This is Phil Clark."

"Phil?" Mr Hall's voice was friendly but surprised.

"Sorry to trouble you, but it's about the Saturday job. Did you mean what you said about wanting help?"

Mr Hall laughed. "I always want help!"

"Would it be all right if I came down next Saturday morning?" Phil asked. He was holding the telephone tight, the receiver clamped against his ear until it hurt, but he was surprised how easy it was to ask, after all.

"All right?" Mr Hall said. "Saturday morning, Saturday afternoon, all day Sunday . . . come whenever you like!"

"Mr Hall!" Phil was laughing too. "I didn't know you were such a slave driver!"

"You wait!" Mr Hall said. "You'll be down then?"

"I'll be down," Phil promised. "What time?"

"Oh . . . not too early. Say about five in the morning?"

"What!" Phil said, horrified. Then he heard Mr Hall laughing, and felt his chest fill with the warmth of his own laughter.

"Five o'clock!" Phil repeated in mock derision. "Do me a favour!"

"Any time, Phil," Mr Hall said. "Any time!" □

124

A S the train glided out of Paddington for the West Country, Oliver Bruce was thinking about his daughter Jean's last letter: "Guess who's come back to live in Cotshill in one of the new single flats in Cherry Crescent," she had written. "A Mrs Mary Stevens, who — I understand from local gossip — was originally Mary Blair, sweetheart of the county. I can well believe it!

"I saw her in the library the other day and in spite of the thirty years' advantage I went home and threw out the old frock I'd been wearing and booked a perm!

"We had a little chat, she seemed to remember you quite clearly. Do you remember her, and if so were you smitten like the rest of the male population?

"Anyway, it will be someone for you to look up when you visit us, Dad. We're really looking forward to seeing you. Unfortunately Bob has to be away some of the time on a course, but he'll see you before he goes. And Susie can't wait to introduce you to her new pet . . ."

GRANDAD'S GIRL

That's what he called his little granddaughter. Forgetting that someone else had prior claim to the title . . .

125

GRANDAD'S GIRL

Oliver was looking forward with pleasant anticipation to his stay with Jean in the village where he had been brought up. He'd always got on well with his son-in-law and little Susie was his pride and delight. Not that little now, of course. She was almost 10.

She'd been only two when his dear wife, Louise, had died. Dear Louise, she'd never been strong, but he loved her, and taking care of her had been a pleasure, not a burden. With her love and support he'd gone from a self-conscious, rather clumsy and introverted boy into a quiet yet confident man.

All things considered, their life together had been very happy.

His thoughts returned to the letter, and the mention of Mary. He was glad Jean had only been teasing, and hadn't guessed he'd been as dizzy about Mary as the rest! He'd had just one chance with Mary, and bungled it from sheer nerves.

There'd been a moonlight summer picnic, and Mary's partner and his date for the evening hadn't turned up. Mary had sat down beside him and begun to talk about a book he'd been reading.

He knew it was only kindness that prompted her action because he always seemed to be alone, but she stayed close and later he found himself walking her home.

Any other young man would have tried to draw her into the shadow and claim a goodnight kiss, but that wasn't his way. And he would have hated to see a glint of amusement in those lovely dark eyes. Besides . . . he was just too shy.

Mary had been a delightful, unattainable dream. She had married Gerald Stevens, a theatrical producer who had come briefly to Cotshill to visit friends and went away before Oliver met Louise. Then when Jean was grown up and newly married to Bob, Oliver and Louise left Cotshill for London where Oliver, now a solicitor, was offered a position in a group practice.

T HE train ran into a tunnel and Oliver eyed his reflection in the dark window. His thinning hair was neatly brushed back with distinctive wings of grey over each ear.

He gave his reflection a shame-faced grin before it vanished with daylight at the end of the tunnel. Thinking of impressing Mary? he asked himself dryly.

But it would be rather gratifying to let her see what he'd made of himself — the boy who couldn't speak to girls without stammering a little, and always managed to tread on their toes or spill something on their dresses.

Jean and Susie were at the station to meet him. Susie flew up the platform, arms wide, and flung herself at him.

"Grandad, come and see who's waiting in the car! Mummy wouldn't let me bring him out in case he got away. Hurry, I'm dying to show you."

"Easy, Susie," Jean chided, kissing and greeting Oliver.

"I can't wait to meet this new member of the family," Oliver said cheerfully. "Is he furry or feathery? And what's his name? I hope he doesn't bite!"

He lives in a cage, but he's not a bird!" Susie laughed gleefully at puzzling him. "He could bite, I s'pose, if he's frightened, but mostly he just nibbles. And I want you to choose a name for him, Grandad." She lifted a furry object from a cardboard box on the seat of the car.

"Would you like to hold him?" she asked her grandfather.

"Don't let him loose in the car," Jean warned sternly, stowing Oliver's suitcase. "I don't want him causing an accident."

"He's a hamster," Susie said proudly. Oliver gazed at the little ball of golden fur. His idea of a pet was something larger. Even now he was still clumsy with small things.

"How about calling him Honey?" he suggested. "He's the same colour."

"Belinda's hamster is called Honey," Susie said quickly.

"Harold? Hubert? Hector?"

"They're all ordinary," Susie said disappointedly. "Jenny's is called Hammy, Wendy called hers Goldie — I want something extra special."

"Has there been an epidemic of hamsters?" Oliver asked Jean.

"You could call it that," Jean replied. "Andrea started it, she's always first with everything.

"Still, it could have been worse, Andrea's father might have bought her an elephant for her birthday, I suppose."

They all laughed.

"What about calling him Hannibal?" Oliver exclaimed, inspired by Jean's remark. "He was a great general, Susie, he led a whole string of elephants over the Alps."

Susie liked the sound of that, though the diminutive ball of fur didn't look particularly impressed. "I think I'll start a Hamster Club," she announced.

Oliver looked critically at his daughter as she sat opposite him at the evening meal.

"You look tired, Jean. Are you all right?"

"She's been overworking," Bob answered. "She's so obliging, people depend on her too much. She's practically carried the weight of the fête this year."

"I can't let people down, Bob," Jean said with a tight smile.

Her tone was slightly irritable, which was also unlike Jean, and Oliver stayed tactfully silent, resolving to help wherever he could.

T HE day of the fête, Jean went on ahead to the cricket field where it was being held and Susie escorted Oliver. Once there, he renewed his acquaintance with Belinda, Susie's best friend, and a number of other children who welcomed him like an old friend. All chattering at the same time, they pulled him from stall to stall.

GRANDAD'S GIRL

He threw darts and won a golliwog, which he gave to Belinda's little brother. He lobbed balls at coconuts and missed hopelessly.

Suddenly the children wanted pony rides, and he found himself guardian of a sticky candyfloss, a melting ice-cream and of course, the golliwog.

"You look as if you need three hands. Would you like me to hold Golly while you eat your ice-cream? It's melting!"

He spun round to meet Mary's teasing eyes, sparkling and mischievous as they had been 45 years ago, he remembered.

"It — it isn't mine," he said, furious to feel the extra colour rise to his heated cheeks, not to mention the stammer he thought he'd lost for good. "It's Benjy's." He pointed towards the small boy sitting astride a grey pony.

"He's going to be unlucky unless that pony gets a move on," she laughed. "Most of it's dripped on to your trousers."

As he tilted the cone upright, the candy-floss fell off the stick into a sugary lump on the grass.

"Oh dear. Still the same walking disaster area I always was," he said quickly. "Remember when I accidentally turned up the bunsen-burner and blew up the chemistry master's experiment?" he joked, desperately trying to regain his composure.

She chuckled.

"That was marvellous — we only wished you'd blown up the whole lab! Those of us who were no good at science, anyway." Her bright eyes regarded him steadily.

"How are you, Oliver? It's good to see you again after all these years."

"I'm fine. And you?" He wanted to tell her she looked wonderful, but the words seemed to stick in his throat.

"Well and happy, thank you."

"I never imagined you'd return to a sleepy place like this —" he began, but was overwhelmed at that point by the returning children.

"I'm afraid I'll have to visit the ice-cream and candy-floss stalls now," he broke off. "But I hope we'll meet again soon."

And she had smiled that wonderful smile as they parted.

ON the way home he thought of all the things he'd imagined saying and asking, and railed at himself for the way he'd been so tongue-tied. ". . . so will you make up a puzzle for our magazine, Grandad?" Susie's eager voice broke into his reverie.

"What sort of puzzle?" He dragged his thoughts away from Mary.

"Anything you like. Belinda and I have decided our Hamster Club must have a magazine and competitions and things. You could judge the first one for us, Grandad."

Jean arrived home late, looking pale and harassed.

"Go and lie down, my dear," he suggested. "I'll bring you a nice cup of tea."

"Oh, Dad, that would be lovely."

"You stay there as long as you like. I'll look after Susie," he reassured her when he brought the tea-tray upstairs.

The next day she had a temperature and looked so ill that Oliver called in the doctor.

"A severe attack of the summer 'flu," the doctor diagnosed.

"What a time for it to happen," Jean moaned. "Bob away and you here for a holiday . . ."

"Now stop worrying," he reassured. "I'm quite self-reliant."

"But the place is such a mess. I've been so busy." She put her hand to her head. "And there's the shopping . . ."

"That'll do!" Oliver commanded sternly. "Just lie back, Susie and I will see to everything."

On Monday he made a list and set off for the supermarket. The place was packed, mainly with mothers and toddlers. He got a trolley but soon wished he hadn't, for it seemed to have a mind of its own.

Concentrating on the steering, he missed the baked beans without which Susie seemed unable to exist. He tried to reverse.

"It's easier if you do another tour around the block!" a laughing voice said, after he'd held up the traffic flow and almost upset a free-standing basket of special offers in the aisle. Red-faced, he turned to see Mary, her eyes twinkling.

"What did you forget, Oliver?" She smiled gaily. "I'll find it. I'm used to this place now."

When they emerged, he was weighed down by two plastic carriers sagging ominously.

"Monday's a bad day to come usually, they have special offers to attract the shoppers who used to come on Saturdays. My car's round the corner. I was going on to visit a friend. Why don't you let me drive you home, Oliver?"

"That was very good of you," he said, as he alighted at Jean's gate. "Thanks a lot. We seem fated to meet at awkward times." He hesitated for a second, then continued. "I would like to have a long chat, Mary."

"I always go to the library on Wednesday mornings," she smiled. "Perhaps we could meet there."

They fixed a time and he waved cheerfully, till the car was gone.

He unloaded the groceries without seeing what he was doing. He'd been slow off the mark. He could have asked her in for coffee.

He could ask Mary out to lunch on Wednesday, though. He noticed the old Bell Inn had expanded and was advertising bar lunches. Susie would be at school for lunch.

His daughter was gradually improving, and on Wednesday he left her with a jug of fresh orange and some tiny tempting sandwiches and a letter from Bob.

"Thanks Dad, you're a dear. Now off you go and have a nice time."

He noticed a faint curiosity in the heavy-lidded eyes and made a quick exit. Mary wasn't there when he reached the library and he exchanged Jean's book and had a browse.

GRANDAD'S GIRL

When Mary hadn't appeared by one-thirty he decided she wasn't coming. She'd probably forgotten, he thought sadly.

That afternoon he cleaned out the garden shed for Bob, and when Susie came home, helped her with her magazine plans.

"What shall we give for a prize for the competition?" she asked him.

"I'll buy some chocolate if you like," Oliver suggested.

"Oh, that'd be nice, but we ought to give the winner's hamster something as well, because it's their magazine."

"Sunflower seeds?" he suggested.

"They eat those all the time. I know — a trip round the fort!"

"Daddy's old one he had when he was little. It's in the attic. Could we get it down and clean it while you've still got your old garden clothes on?"

Oliver was up among the dusty rafters when the doorbell rang.

"I'll go," Susie cried from the landing.

Oliver carefully manoeuvred the fort to the trap door.

Susie came running back up the stairs.

"Who was it, Susie?" he called.

"Mrs Stevens. She said to tell you she was sorry about this morning, but an old friend called un'spectedly to take her to lunch."

"She hasn't gone, has she?" Oliver cried.

"Yes, because I said Mummy was in bed and you were very busy," she said, pleased she'd remembered everything.

He looked down at his dusty clothes and dirty hands and despaired. Were they never to meet under normal circumstances?

O VER the next few days he looked out for Mary, but she seemed to have gone into hibernation. Jean was still in bed, but much perkier, and he decided to ask a few tentative questions.

"I was passing Cherry Crescent yesterday." His voice was deliberately casual. "Didn't you say Mary lived at number six? She didn't seem to be around."

"No?" Jean considered. "I seem to remember she was spending a week with friends sometime this month. She gets around, you know. Heaps of friends all over the place."

"Yes," he agreed with a small sigh. Why should Oliver Bruce be any more important to her now than he'd ever been? He tried to push these self-pitying thoughts aside.

"By the way, Jean, is it all right if Susie has some friends round one day next week? I'd keep an eye on everything. It's this Hamster Club, she wants a meeting on the back lawn."

Jean gave a feeble grin.

"Every few weeks there's some new craze. Still, it keeps them out of mischief . . ."

"My only worry is conducting the winning hamster on a trip round Bob's old fort," he told his daughter. "After a week's acquaintance with

130

Hannibal I've decided that hamsters are very unpredictable."

"No wonder you and Susie get on so well, you're as crazy as she is." Jean lay back on her pillows. "Let's hope I'll be well enough to help."

T HE party was fixed for Thursday, after school. During the class, Oliver gave serious consideration to the competition entries and decided upon the winner.

"Annette!" Susie exclaimed when he told her of his decision. "Oh, she's got Hector."

Oliver sensed reservations.

"Is something the matter with that?" He tried to hide a smile.

"He's a bit of a troublemaker. Some hamsters are, you know," Susie told him knowledgeably.

"Well, that's all right, they'll all be in cages. They can squabble through the bars," Oliver said cheerfully.

He wasn't to know that Wendy would arrive with Goldie in her pocket. And Jenny brought her chittering Hammy in a dilapidated shoe box with very large air holes.

The fort was a focus of great interest and Annette made a generous gesture. "So long as Hector can see round it first, the others can have a look as well."

"One at a time," Oliver cautioned, as the fort was thrown

CARING

*It's wonderful when someone needs
A friendly, helping hand,
And thanks you with a grateful heart,
Because you understand.
It's wonderful the feeling that
You have a part to play,
However small or humble,
It means something every day.
It's wonderful when folk are glad
Because they know you're near,
That in these now uncertain times,
The star of hope shines clear.
Remember, there's no time to feel
Unwanted or alone,
For when you know you're needed,
Then the way ahead is shown!*

— Mrs E. G., Herts.

open to the hamster public. But while he was in the kitchen replenishing the orange juice jug, things literally got out of hand.

Jean, who was up but keeping clear at Oliver's stern insistence, poked her head out of the sitting-room door as an alarmed squeal rent the air. Voices rose excitedly.

"What's going on? Dad, I can't stay here any longer, I must . . . oh, there's the doorbell, I'll answer it. Go and she what's happening, for heaven's sake!"

Oliver ran out to find wild confusion. The lawn was covered in darting furry bodies.

Anxious little girls were making ineffectual grabs which only excited the hamsters more.

Oliver set down the jug hastily, sloshing a wave of orange juice down

131

his shirt, and dived into the fray. He captured a handful of creamy fur which objected loudly. It was Hector.

"Annette — take him, will you — Oh! Mary!" He stopped short and stared at the startled figure of Mary Stevens.

Jean, who had conducted her visitor into the garden, clapped both hands to her face in horror. And Mary Stevens, the composed belle of Cotshill, never before seen at a loss, turned white, dropped her handbag and leaped with great agility on to the rustic garden seat.

"Oh! Oliver! Take me away! Quickly!" she squeaked.

Without stopping to think, Oliver swept Mary off the seat and into his arms and carried her to the safety of the kitchen.

Here he set her down, hastily overcome by his own impetuous behaviour.

"I'm sorry," Mary gasped. "It's just — anything little, mouse-like, I can't bear. Silly, I know, but . . ."

"Don't apologise, I have qualms myself when they show me their teeth," Oliver answered her. He glanced through the window where Jean had joined in the chase.

"It seems to be under control apart from the bit of stalking in the rose bed.

"What say we stay in here and make a cup of tea?"

"Oh, Oliver," she said, collapsing into a chair. "I think you're marvellous." To his astonishment he saw genuine admiration on her face.

"Mary, I've been trying to impress you ever since I came here. I'm so glad I've done the right thing at the right time at last!"

"Impress me?" Her big eyes were genuinely puzzled. "Oliver, you've always impressed me right from school days. Always your own man, never going along with the sheep for the sake of it."

"But . . . you were always so popular, so much in demand," he exclaimed disbelieving.

"Oh, yes, I was a proper little flirt!" She laughed, a hint of colour in her cheeks making her look prettier than ever. "Do you know, I was quite piqued that night you walked me home from the picnic, and didn't even attempt to kiss me. The vanity of it all!" she mocked herself gently.

Then in a quiet voice she surprised Oliver with her next few words.

"Tell me, Oliver, what was your wife like?"

"Louise? Dark, gentle, of delicate health. But we had twenty-four extremely happy years before her final illness."

"I'm sure you looked after her wonderfully," Mary said wistfully. "Gerald and I parted after only four years. It was a mutual agreement. Staying together wouldn't have worked and we both knew it. But seeing you with Jean and Susie I know I've missed such a lot. "

"You're welcome to a stake in anything I've got," he told her lightly, and then realised what he'd said. But he did not qualify it nor did he feel embarrassed.

"And I promise you," he said smiling broadly, "that doesn't include hamsters!" □

132

WHEN TITUS CAME TO TOWN

Life was never quite the same again. When it came to sorting out people's lives, he wasn't one for pussy-footing around.

Complete Story by STELLA WHITELAW

I T was not that Titus was stage-struck or came from a theatrical family of cats, he simply came upon the warm, steamy stage door entrance of the theatre by chance on a chilly October night. The Titus of that moment was far removed from the majestic creature who now greets patrons in the foyer of the plush theatre as they arrive for the evening performance.

He always sits a little to the side of the first step of the grand staircase leading to the Dress Circle, his brilliant lemon eyes scrutinising each new arrival.

But on that wet, autumn night, Titus slunk his emaciated body towards the stage door, drawn like a magnet towards the light and warmth.

His long fur was matted, his coat caked with Thames mud, and one ear was tattered and bloodied after a fight with some Soho cats over the debris from a restaurant dustbin.

Titus had been on the London streets for 27 days. It had been a terrifying experience, and one for which his suburban upbringing had not prepared him.

133

WHEN TITUS CAME TO TOWN

From kittenhood he had been fed and housed by the Carson family, and comfortably quartered in a specially-designed cat-bed elegantly lined with foam cushions. Life had been uneventful apart from pouncing on the odd bird, or having an occasional night out on the prowl.

Titus had been sunning himself one day when he gathered vaguely that the Carsons were going on something called a half-term holiday. He sensed change in the bustle of packing and kept out of the way.

Then the Carsons discovered that the cat kennels had closed because of a flu epidemic.

This seemed to throw everyone in a panic, and Titus, who somehow felt responsible, kept very quiet and remained withdrawn.

Then an old aunt appeared with an equally old wicker basket and said why couldn't they take Titus with them to the house they were renting in Cornwall?

Titus had sniffed the basket with apprehension. It smelled of long-gone cats, ill cats, bored cats, tired cats. When they put him inside it, he fought and scratched and it took two adults to fasten the lid.

All the way to London in the car, Titus spat and howled and they had to turn up the volume on the radio to drown his protests. Nerves began to get frayed and the children started to quarrel about silly things.

Titus scratched and chewed between howls. Suddenly the lid flew up and he scrambled out. He perched for one petrified moment on the back of the driver's seat and then leapt out of the open car window.

The cacophony of noise was terrifying. Buses, cars, coaches, hooters blaring from all directions . . . Titus fled along Westminster Bridge, careering between people's legs, dashing across the road, slithering down stone steps and racing along the Embankment, his tail high and fur on end.

The Carsons could not find him. They spent an agonising two hours searching and calling his name. Eventually they gave up and continued on their way to Cornwall. Both children cried noisily in the back of the car.

TITUS crawled out from his hiding place under a fruit stall near Charing Cross Underground Station and surveyed the busy street scene. It was nothing like the town he came from. At first he felt a little heady and elated with his new freedom, and he strolled the streets, gazing around like a tourist.

But three days later the excitement of city life had worn off. He was cold and hungry and there was hostility from other vagrant cats.

If he found a restaurant dustbin with some fish or chicken in it, within seconds some big-boned feline would turn up, hissing and spitting and claiming territorial rights.

The weather changed and it began to rain, and warm places were difficult to find. How hard the pavement was on his paws, and his pads grew calluses.

Titus was not built for jungle warfare. His plump good looks melted away and he became scrawny and distrusting. No-one spoke to him and he missed the sound of a human voice. No-one stroked him with affection. His very heart shrank with emptiness.

Titus roamed the mud flats of the Thames shore, wondering if it might lead to this place called Cornwall.

He had had nothing to eat on the 27th day except a rotting fish head he had found in a gutter near Billingsgate Market.

He crouched against a wall where overhanging stonework gave him some protection from the weather.

He watched the lights of the stage door entrance, and the orangey-red glow from within. It looked warm and he could hear cheerful sounds.

People were coming out now, chatting and laughing.

"Night-night. Sleep tight."

"On my diet? See you tomorrow."

Titus wondered if he might be able to slip in unnoticed when the next group of people paused in the doorway before venturing out into the grey street. He slithered forward, his shape merging into the dark shadows of the night.

"Just look at that poor creature," one of the young women said suddenly. She came out of the group, not heeding the rain on her fair, curling hair. She did not touch Titus, but went down on one knee, approaching him respectfully.

She made small encouraging noises so that he would not be alarmed, and when he made no move to escape or bite, she put out a careful hand to rub his forehead.

"There, there, puss. My goodness, you are wet — and so thin. Look, Nigel, you can see his ribs. I don't think the poor thing has had a decent meal for weeks."

"Oh, do come along, Lindy. Stop messing about with that revolting creature."

Nigel strolled over, a tall elegant young man turning up the collar of his trench-coat.

"It doesn't seem fair," Lindy said, straightening up. "Here we are, going out to supper when we're not really hungry, leaving this poor cat who's starving. It's cruel."

"What do you propose we do? Take the cat out to supper with us? Do you think it would fancy Chinese or Italian?" he asked with a calculated degree of sarcasm in his voice. He was a very promising actor.

"That's a splendid idea," Lindy said with some spirit. "You go ahead and join the others. I'm taking him across to Joe's for a good, square meal."

"You must be joking, Lindy. For heaven's sake, you're not going to pick it up? It's filthy and it's probably got fleas. It'll bite you and then you'll get a cat fever. And we've no-one to replace you if you get cat fever," Nigel warned gloomily.

"Nonsense, he's not going to bite me. He's got the look of a perfect gentleman. And you'd be filthy, too, if you were living in the streets. He's a gorgeous cat really. Look at his eyes. They're beautiful . . ."

WHEN TITUS CAME TO TOWN

Titus did not struggle. The young woman's arms were holding him confidently, and she spoke soft words of comfort.

Joe's Café was on the point of closing, but when Joe Bronowski saw Lindy coming in, he hastily reversed his closed sign.

"Hi, there," he said, casually stacking his accountancy books out of sight under the counter. He was taking a correspondence course between customers. "What can I get you?"

"One coffee and one warm milk straightaway, please, Joe. Then one cottage pie with plenty of gravy and I think I'll just have a cheese omelette," Lindy said, choosing a table away from the door and the draughts. She settled the cat on her knee.

"Eating alone?" Joe asked, slightly confused by the order.

"No, Titus is joining me," Lindy said, adding to Joe's confusion.

How Titus enjoyed that first meal with Lindy. The warm milk was nectar, the cottage pie ambrosia. He could hardly eat for the deep, rhythmic purrs that threatened to choke him.

Afterward Lindy took him back to the theatre, explaining that he could not live in her high-rise flat, but that he was welcome to doss down in her dressing-room.

She found him an old props box and lined it with paper towels. She thoughtfully left open a small top window so that he could get out.

Titus fell asleep, hardly able to believe his luck. He felt his dignity returning as he warmed to this strange, rambling building where people seemed to live during the day but go away at night, leaving it all to him.

NOT only did Titus adopt the theatre, but he appointed himself Lindy's guardian. He also took on the task of getting the theatre into shape. He swept it clean of mice. He checked security, superintended the cleaning women, attended rehearsals, and was in the foyer every evening to welcome the patrons.

His appearance improved out of all recognition . . . he was not only clean and well fed, but he had grown in magnificence with his new status.

His fur was clean and fluffy, and his coat gleamed. He held his head proudly, his shoulders haunched haughtily, his tail curved over his toes with precision and delicacy. His lemon eyes watched everybody and everything. Nothing escaped him.

Titus ate at Joe's Café where Lindy insisted that Joe give her a weekly bill. Joe was reluctant to hand over the bill, saying that Titus mainly had left-overs, but Lindy was adamant. What about all the extra milk?

Titus guessed that Joe did not charge Lindy enough because there was often a nice piece of fish or some steak for him. So he took on the café as a sideline and their mice got a salutary heave-ho.

But it was noticed that Titus had a curious attitude towards the cats who scavenged the dustbins. He sent them flying, but not, Joe observed, until after they had found something to eat.

"It's as if Titus remembers," Joe told Lindy, one evening over late coffee. "He seems to have a certain sympathy for them."

136

"Of course he remembers," Lindy said, rubbing Titus expertly under his chin. "Cats have memories. They are really intelligent creatures."

It was in Lindy's dressing-room that Titus overheard Lindy and Nigel having a fairly heated discussion about the play. It was a classic thriller and assured of a pretty long run because of the tourists and coach parties. But Lindy was unhappy about one scene.

"The letter incident really is my best scene," Lindy was saying as she sat at the mirror taking off her make-up. "And I would appreciate it if you would not fidget so much, Nigel."

Titus was only half listening. He was curled up in his prop box, which was now lined with Lindy's shawl.

"I'm not fidgeting," Nigel said, lighting up a cigarette. "I'm merely being natural and at ease."

"I don't regard that messing about with the decanter this evening as being natural and at ease. How can I be tense and emotional, reading the letter, when you are wandering about doing different things?"

"It wouldn't be so bad if you always did the same things, then at least I could time my pauses."

"I'm improvising," Nigel said casually. "You should be able to cope."

Lindy turned, the amber in her eyes starting to spark.

"I don't rush about madly during your confession scene," she retorted. "I keep still, I blend, I merge. I leave it to you. It's your scene."

"But that's your style," Nigel said, rising from his seat. "You blend and merge . . . I just naturally dominate."

"Oh!" The crash of the jar of cleansing cream made Titus almost jump out of his box. "How can you be so selfish?" Lindy stormed at Nigel.

"You're spoiling my best part! People will stop believing in me, and then when the contracts are renewed, they'll get somebody else . . ."

Titus did not understand about contracts but he knew all about being out on the streets. He had had 27 days of it and he would not wish one half-minute of his experience on his beloved Lindy.

THE following evening, once the audience was seated and he had checked the Stalls, the Dress Circle and the Upper Circle, Titus sat in the wings keeping well out of everyone's way. It was true. During the letter scene, Nigel very craftily took the tension out of Lindy's reading. He stretched, he got up to close the curtains, he smoothed his hair in a mirror . . .

Lindy's hand was trembling as she held the crucial letter but Titus could tell that the audience had been diverted and the atmosphere in the theatre had lost its electricity.

In the interval he went back to Lindy's dressing room but he didn't go in. From inside he could hear the sound of weeping.

Titus nipped over to Joe's Café, which was unusual. Normally he never left the theatre during a performance. Joe looked up from the textbook he was studying, surprised.

"Hello, you're early," he said. "What's the matter?"

WHEN TITUS CAME TO TOWN

Titus could not tell him, but he tried. He rubbed against Joe's ankles, emitted a sharp, low, desperate miaow, then returned to the theatre.

The confession scene was near the end of the play. It was well-written and Nigel made the most of it. He began the speech with his usual artistry and confidence.

At about line four, Titus casually strolled on to the stage. He sniffed carefully around and then decided that the upholstered arm of the settee was the best vantage spot. He leaped gracefully on to the settee and took up his position. Then he turned and stared at Nigel.

How he stared. He kept still. He remembered what Lindy had said about blending, but it was a little difficult for a magnificent furry cat to blend successfully.

He sat there throughout the whole speech, staring, dignified, enigmatic, ears pricked up to show that he was listening politely to this vaguely amiable idiot.

Nigel fought back. His voice grew louder, his projection more deliberate. The sweat glistened on his forehead.

Then Titus yawned, a small pink-mouthed yawn of delicate boredom. The audience collapsed in laughter.

It did not ruin the play but it did ruin Nigel's scene. He stormed off after the curtain calls in a furious temper.

"I'll kill that cat," he raged. "Get it out of the theatre!"

But the management refused. Everyone liked Titus, and the producer thought the change of emphasis actually improved the finale.

He was wondering if Titus could be persuaded to do it again.

Meanwhile Titus took refuge under the table at Joe's, exhausted. Acting was definitely tiring.

Of course it was in all the newspapers the next day. The box office began to break records as people came to see Titus. He did not always go on. It seemed to depend on how the letter scene went.

Eventually Nigel's nerve broke. He could stand it no longer and he left the cast. Lindy got her contract renewed, Joe passed his exams and a few months later they got married.

Titus went to the wedding reception. He decided wedding cake was over-rated but champagne was delicious. Lindy looked as pretty as a picture with white roses entwined in her dark curls. He hardly recognised Joe in a suit.

"And where are you going for your honeymoon?" somebody asked.

"Cornwall," Lindy said. "We've been lent a very romantic fisherman's cottage. We thought we might take Titus with us."

Titus did a standing leap which took him out of the window on to the balcony of the restaurant. He fled down the Strand, through the back streets of Covent Garden, down an alleyway that led to another alleyway that led to the back of the theatre. In a trice he was through his window, into Lindy's dressing-room and into his prop box.

He loved Lindy. He was prepared to follow her to the ends of the earth — providing it didn't prove to be Cornwall! □

After All These Years

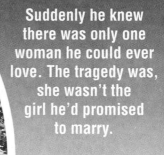

Suddenly he knew there was only one woman he could ever love. The tragedy was, she wasn't the girl he'd promised to marry.

Complete Story by
ISOBEL STEWART

SOMEHOW he hadn't realised just how hard it was going to be, telling Sally. She sat on the floor, cross-legged, her soft brown hair framing her vivid face, her voice warm and laughing.

Sally.

He'd known her all his life. They'd gone to the same school, he'd taught her to ride her first two-wheeled bike. They'd played tennis together and gone to school dances together. She was the first girl he'd kissed and it was her first kiss. On her twentieth birthday, he'd given her the garnet ring that had belonged to his grandmother.

Everyone was delighted — David's folk and Sally's folk had been friends for so long. The wedding wouldn't be until David had qualified, but Sally said the garnet ring made the waiting easier while David was doing his time as a houseman in Bournemouth and they were apart.

Sally.

His girl. The girl he'd asked to marry him, the girl he'd been so sure he would spend the rest of his life with — until he met Katherine.

"Sally," he said abruptly, because suddenly it was unbearable to sit here with her when she didn't know what he had to say to her.

"Oh, dear," she said remorsefully, "I'm sitting here chattering, and you must be tired — driving all through the night, just after coming off duty. I still couldn't believe it when your mother came round to say you'd be up

139

AFTER ALL THESE YEARS

here for the weekend. It's quite mad and impulsive, David — not at all like you!"

She laughed, but he saw now the anxiety in her clear blue eyes.

"Sally," he said quietly and sadly, "there's something I have to tell you."

Her small hands, with his garnet ring on the left one, were suddenly still. "I was afraid you did," she said unsteadily. "I — I think that's why I've kept on talking — so that you wouldn't say it."

"I have to say it," he told her.

She turned away, her hair swinging down, shielding her face.

"What's her name?" she asked him, and the brightness in her voice brought a further ache to his heart. "Is she very beautiful? I suppose she must be. Beautiful and exciting —"

"Sally, stop it!" he said rather too sharply.

He sat down on the floor beside her, and took both her hands in his.

"I wish it didn't have to be like this," he said, his voice low.

"Tell me about her," Sally said, quietly now. And then, when he was silent, she insisted, "David, I think I have a right to know."

He gave in, although there seemed to be something quite wrong about sitting here telling Sally about Katherine.

"She's not beautiful or glamorous at all," he said at last. "She's small and slim with brown eyes and fair hair. She's a nurse. I've known her for quite a while."

"Surely that's not all?" Sally asked after a moment.

No, David thought. That isn't all.

"She has a little boy of two," he said quietly. "His name's Tim. She isn't married."

"Oh, David," Sally murmured, "it can't have been easy for her, and you must feel sorry for her."

It was all too clear what she was saying, and he couldn't leave it at that, even although he hated to say anything that would hurt her more.

"No," he forced himself to say with certainty. "I was in love with her before I knew a single thing about her." And that was true.

He couldn't remember the exact moment when he knew, for it had grown gradually, as they worked together. At first, she was Sister Bennett, who was small and brisk and efficient. Then he began to see that as well as efficiency there was warmth and caring.

One day he found her in the Duty Room comforting a young nurse upset by the first death she'd seen. Over the girl's white cap, David had seen the gleam of tears in Katherine's eyes.

Perhaps, he thought now, that was when it started. He didn't know. At any rate, it wasn't long afterwards that he became aware that his heart lightened and lifted when he came into her ward and saw her, and the few moments he was with her each day became increasingly important and precious to him.

One night, because he knew there was nothing else he could do, he waited for her to come off duty. He knew that she would be walking

140

down to catch the bus on the main road, and he opened his car door and called to her.

"I'll give you a lift, Sister."

He'd intended to be friendly, but professional. But when she turned to him and he saw that she was going to refuse, he'd been unable to hide the urgency in his voice.

"Please, Katherine. I have to talk to you."

She got into the car then, but not before he had seen, by the shadowing of her dark eyes, that she knew how he had come to feel about her.

"Thank you, Doctor Martin," she'd said with careful composure. "I'll appreciate a lift tonight, I'm a bit late picking up my little boy."

Afterwards — long afterwards — she'd admitted that she had said that deliberately, that she had wanted to shock him with the truth.

"Fine," he had replied, his voice as cool as hers had been. "I'll take you there, just tell me where it is."

That night, when the little boy, Tim, had been bathed and fed and asleep, and Katherine, still on her guard, had made omelettes for them, they had talked and talked for hours.

Katherine had told him quite steadily, making no excuses, about the man she'd been in love with; the man who had never, she realised too late, had anything as permanent as marriage in his mind. But she had completed her training, and she had kept her baby.

David, in his turn, had told her about Sally. Katherine had listened quietly, her brown eyes serious.

"She sounds a lovely person, David," she'd said softly.

"She is," David had agreed, and he'd meant it.

Katherine had said, then, quickly, unsteadily, that she thought he'd better go.

"It isn't late," he'd replied.

"It is," she'd said, a little desperately. "It's too late already."

AND it was too late. Before he'd even kissed her, before he'd held her in his arms, it was too late. He loved her. And she loved him. He knew that, although she refused to admit it then and for some time. Until then, love for him had meant Sally — Sally, sweet and pretty and warm and laughing. Sally soft in his arms, her lips warm against his.

Loving Katherine was different, in so many ways. There was still laughter, there was still lightness in their loving, but gradually, surely, he saw that there was a depth and a completeness and a rightness about the way he felt for Katherine, that there had not been with Sally.

"David," Sally said now, and his heart ached at the effort behind the careful steadiness of her voice, "thank you for coming to tell me, and not just writing."

"I had to come," he replied awkwardly. "It's bad enough doing this — it would have been worse by letter."

He'd done some thinking, between Bournemouth and Newcastle, some necessary thinking on practical points.

AFTER ALL THESE YEARS

"You must be the one to break our engagement, Sally," he told her, and difficult as it was, he couldn't look away, he couldn't turn from the hurt in her eyes. "You can just tell people that it hasn't worked, me being away, or perhaps that you feel you need time before settling down. Anything — whatever you like, I don't mind. And," he hesitated, but he had to say it, "I would like you to keep the ring."

Sally was staring straight ahead of her.

"No," she said clearly, emphatically.

"It's really just a dress ring," he said awkwardly, "and . . ."

She shook her head.

"That isn't what I mean," she told him. "I'm not talking about the ring, David. I'm saying that I won't just break off our engagement."

"Do you mean you want me to do it?" he asked her. "I thought this would be the best way, easier all round."

"No," Sally said again.

Suddenly, he had a vivid memory of a small, chubby Sally at the steps of the big swimming pool, deciding that she wasn't going to go in. There was the same look of mutiny on Sally's face now.

"What do you mean?" he asked her.

She lifted her chin, and looked at him steadily.

"I mean that I'm giving you time to think, David. I mean that I'm not going to let you do this — I'm not going to let you hurt your parents, or throw away our future, or forget all the years we've known each other. In fairness to yourself, as well as to me, David, I won't let you."

He stared at her, shaken and appalled, for this was a reaction he'd never imagined.

"Now wait a minute, Sally," he began.

"No, you wait a minute, and you listen to me, David," she returned. "All the years we've known each other, all the plans we've made . . . I don't like to put it this way, David, but I think you owe me something, and I want you to give yourself time. Think about it, and don't do anything yet. Please, David."

If she had wept or thrown herself into his arms, he would have been able to refuse, he thought later. But she did nothing like that. Instead, she stood in front of him, her chin held high.

"I'm not asking much, David," she said quietly. "Just that you give us time. Don't say anything to your parents, or to mine."

He looked down at her.

"I won't change my mind, Sally," he told her gently.

"Possibly not," she agreed after a moment. "But at least, David, I'll feel that you've given us a chance." She turned away, then. "I'm going for a walk on the beach," she said, and now there was an unsteadiness in her voice. "I'll come round later, David — your mum asked me to come for lunch. And please, think about what I've said."

He thought about it. Everything in him longed to be honest, to bring his love for Katherine into the open. But at the same time, if Sally needed time to accept this, then perhaps he did owe her that much.

142

Before he left, he promised Sally that for the moment, he would wait. "Just a little while, David," she said unevenly.

AS he drove back to Bournemouth, he wondered if it was going to be even harder telling Katherine what had happened. She knew why he'd gone home.

I'm a moral coward, he told himself bitterly.

He'd planned to drive straight to Katherine's flat with the news that he was free. But now, because he couldn't say that, he drove first to the small cottage he rented in Poole, and he unpacked. Then, just as he was about to leave to go to Katherine, the phone rang.

It was Sally, and he knew from her voice that she wasn't alone, that her parents, or perhaps her sister, were nearby.

"David?" she said brightly. "Great, I hoped I'd catch you. Did you have a good journey? Listen. I'm due a holiday, and the only holiday I want is being near you, so, guess what? I'm coming down to stay with Aunt Margaret for a week or two. I'll see you in a few days."

He wondered as he replaced the receiver if Sally had thought of this before he left, but it didn't matter, really. She was just being Sally. She'd told him that she wasn't letting him go just like that, she'd made it plain that she was going to put up some resistance, and naturally she'd decided that she could do that better on the spot.

At least, he thought, as he parked outside Katherine's flat, I can tell her everything at once.

But it wasn't as hard telling Katherine as he'd expected it to be. When he had finished she was silent.

"I should have insisted," he said, anger at himself making his voice rough. "I told her nothing would change, but now she's coming here, to stay with her aunt, and her aunt's just round the corner from me. I just didn't want to hurt her any more than I had to . . ."

Katherine's hands were warm and reassuring on his.

"I'm so glad, David," she said, and the unexpectedness of this made him draw back. "No, I really am. She's right, you know. You've got to be very, very sure about this."

He held her close to him, her hair soft against his face.

"I am sure, love," he said.

"Taking time to think about it is sensible and realistic — for all our sakes," Katherine went on.

I don't want to be sensible and realistic, David thought, looking at her. I want the whole world to know that I love you, that you're going to be my wife.

"Besides, having Tim doesn't make it any easier — for you and me, I mean," Katherine added.

"As far as I'm concerned, Katherine," he said, his hands tightening around hers, "Tim's part of the package deal. I love him, and I want him for my son just as much as I want you for my wife. You mustn't ever doubt that."

AFTER ALL THESE YEARS

"I don't," Katherine replied, and she smiled. "No, I don't doubt that, David. But it does make things less straightforward, and for all our sakes I'm glad that Sally asked you to wait. I'm glad she's coming to Bournemouth. Because this way, David, you're being fair to everyone, and that's important."

It was important, he accepted that.

Before he left, he went with her to see that the little boy was tucked in. In the dim light from the hall, David could see Tim asleep in his usual position, his well-napkined bottom up in the air, his face pressed into the pillow, his brown hair, so like his mother's, tousled in sleep. Gently, David put the blanket around the child, and tucked him in.

I'll see you soon, Timmy, he promised silently.

He turned away, but not before he found Katherine's eyes on his face, with a wondering love that was almost his undoing. For a moment, he held her close to him, and then he looked down at her.

"It won't be long," he said.

Three days later, he got home from the hospital to find Sally waiting for him in the cottage.

"Hi," she said, a little defensively. "I hope you don't mind but I knew where you kept the key."

She didn't come into his arms, and as they stood looking at each other, a little awkwardly, his heart ached at the wariness in her blue eyes.

"I was going to make a risotto," Sally said then, "but I didn't know if you'd stop off for a bite to eat on the way home from the hospital."

"I came straight back," he told her, and he knew that he was answering her unspoken question — had he been with Katherine? He smiled. "I'd enjoy a risotto. Is there still time to make it?"

"Plenty of time," she assured him, smiling. "We can have a walk on the beach while it's cooking."

For the first time, they didn't walk hand in hand on the beach, and that was sad, but as they walked along, David told her of Katherine's decision that she and David weren't to see each other while Sally was there.

"Apart from at work, of course," Sally said.

MY QUEEN

The Queen lives in a palace
and sits upon her throne,
you live with me in this poor house,
a threadbare chair you own.
You have no golden carriage,
you shop on tired feet
and drag your parcels home with you
along a city street.

Your clothes have all seen better days,
they're worn out now and old,
but still you tend with loving care
each crumpled, dusty fold.
Our palace is at number four
where we have always been,
your subjects are the pots and pans
and to me you are my queen.

— Mr A. R., N. Yorks.

"Well, yes," he agreed, "but we never do see much of each other at work. Katherine's busy, and so am I." He hesitated, but only for a moment. "And now that that's been said, Sally, I don't want to talk about Katherine."

It wasn't that it was possible to put Katherine out of his mind and out of his heart, but to talk about her to Sally seemed an intrusion on something that was deeply personal and private. He would go along with Sally in this, he thought, but he knew, with complete certainty, how things were going to be.

If Sally needed time to accept it, he would give her time. But he was sure nothing would change.

THEY were busy at the hospital, as always, and often it was later than expected when he got back to the cottage. But Sally was always waiting, and his heart sank at the way her face lit up when she greeted him.

At first she said nothing about their engagement, nothing about his wish to be released from it. They had dinner with her aunt and uncle, then they went to see a ballet. They had coffee afterwards, and talked.

And when they parted, Sally stood on tiptoe, and her lips brushed his briefly, warmly, tentatively. And when she'd gone, and he was alone, David's thoughts were always with Katherine in her small flat. Katherine and Tim, alone as he was alone.

The brief moments when he and Katherine were together in the hospital became even more precious to him.

Short as these times were, they were real, while the time he spent with Sally, he knew with sadness, was not. He was going through the motions, and Sally, too, was unlike herself, so unlike herself that there was a constant ache in his heart for the carefree Sally he had known. It was his fault and yet what else could he have done once he'd met Katherine?

Sally had been in Bournemouth for a week, and they were sitting out on the step of her aunt's house, with the sound of the sea close to them.

"David," she said, as if she had come to a sudden decision, "if you hadn't met her, we would have got married, and we would have been happy. Wouldn't we?"

He was silent, thrown by this.

"Wouldn't we?" Sally insisted. "Think of how happy we were six months ago, when you were home. We would have gone on being happy like that, I know we would, if only you hadn't met her."

He shook his head.

"You can't live on that basis, Sally," he said gently. "I did meet Katherine, and we have to go on from there."

She turned away, but not before he'd seen the gleam of tears in her eyes.

"Sally," he said, all at once weary of the falseness of this, "Sally, don't you think that —?"

But she didn't let him go on.

K

AFTER ALL THESE YEARS

"You know what I think, David," she reminded him. "I think you need to think about this, so that you don't do anything you'll regret later." She brushed the back of her hand across her eyes, impatiently, and the childish gesture tore at his heart. "I'm not enjoying this, you know, being with you, and knowing so well that you're miles away from me."

And then, brightly she said she was going to put the kettle on for coffee, and the next moment her aunt and uncle were with them and the chance had gone. If it had actually been a chance, David thought as he walked down to his cottage later, for Sally, sweet as she was, could be very stubborn.

He woke up the next morning tired, from sleeping badly, but slowly, certainly, the conviction grew that he shouldn't wait until it was time for Sally to go back home. He had got to make her see right now, that he knew what he was doing. Tonight, he thought, I'll talk to her.

It was a busy day at the hospital, and although he had patients to see in Katherine's ward, he didn't get there until the day was almost over.

There was no sign of Katherine in the ward or in the Duty Room. When David had seen his patients, he looked back into the Duty Room.

"Sister Bennett off already?" he asked.

The Staff Nurse shook her head.

"She isn't in today, Doctor Martin," she said. "Her little boy is ill, I think."

He'd promised Katherine that he wouldn't go to her while Sally was here, but as he drove out of the hospital grounds, his concern was as much for the little boy as for Katherine herself.

WHEN Katherine opened the door, her eyes were anxious, and her hair damp on her forehead. "How's Tim? What's wrong with him?" he asked her.

"He's all right now," she said, sounding tired. "It was croup, but a bad attack, David." She tried to smile. "I suppose I panicked because it was Tim."

He followed her through to the small bedroom where the little boy was asleep in his cot. Swiftly, professionally, he checked him, and when he was satisfied, he turned back to Katherine.

"He's all right," he agreed, quietly.

He saw now that she was completely exhausted, and he guessed that she'd been up for most of the night, alone and worried.

"Katherine, love," he said gently, "come here."

She came into his arms and he held her close, knowing that at this moment this was all she needed, the assurance and the security of his love. And as he held her, he made up his mind.

"Pack a case for you and for Tim," he told her. "I'm taking you over to the cottage. Both you and Tim will get over this much sooner with the sea air."

"But Sally?" she asked him.

His arms tightened around her.

146

"I'll take you and Tim to the cottage," he told her, "and then I'll go and tell Sally that you're there. And we'll take it from there."

Tim slept in her arms as they drove towards the sea. It was only when the car stopped beside the cottage that he stirred. David got out of the car, and went round to take the drowsy child from his mother's arms. As he lifted Tim gently, Katherine looked at him and smiled.

Despite the weariness on her face, the love and the trust in her brown eyes held him still. For that moment, there was nothing in the world but the woman and the child he loved.

"Everything's going to be all right," he promised her.

"I know," she replied.

They went into the cottage, and put Tim on one of the beds in the tiny spare room. Katherine opened the window, and the fresh air, cool and healing, filled the room.

"I'll get him settled, David," she said. "When you get back, we can talk."

When I get back from seeing Sally, he thought. He kissed Katherine, gently at first, and then not at all gently.

He went out of the cottage, and turned to the path that would take him quickly to the main road, and Sally's aunt's house. But at the corner, Sally was waiting for him.

"I saw you and Katherine, and the little boy," she said without preamble.

"He's been ill — that's why I brought them here," David began. "I was coming to tell you, Sally, and to tell you —"

"You don't have to say it," she said quickly. "You don't have to say anything, David. I saw the way you looked at her. You haven't ever looked at me like that, David."

There was no accusation in the weary young voice, only acceptance, at last.

"I'm sorry, Sally," he said, meaning it.

There was too much honesty, too much integrity in her, to allow her to pretend it didn't hurt.

"Some day," he began, not sure what he wanted to say.

She nodded.

"Oh, yes," she agreed and she tried to smile. "I don't feel too good right now, but I don't intend to pine away with a broken heart." And then the attempt at a smile was gone.

"Maybe some day I'll find someone who will look at me the way you looked at her. But it won't be you, David."

Without another word, she turned away, and walked down the path to the beach.

He wanted to say something, to call after her. But he knew, with sadness, that right now the only thing he could do for her was to let her walk away from him with her head held high.

He watched until she was out of sight and then he went back to the cottage where Katherine was waiting for him. ☐

Day Of Reckoning

It began like so many things — with the click of the letterbox . . .

THE letter was waiting when I arrived home from work. I didn't need to look at the postmark to know it was from Guy. His writing is unmistakable, that quick scrawl that looks as if he can hardly take time to form the letters properly.

I didn't open it right away. Instead, I let the dog out into the garden, peeled potatoes for Adam coming in from school and prepared a salad. Meanwhile, the letter sat there on the shelf with the chipped paint, accusingly, threateningly, until I had to fetch the paperknife and slit it open.

Twenty minutes later, the contents still hadn't sunk in, not completely.

I want a divorce, Louise.

He wants a divorce, he's not coming back, not ever. The last six months haven't just been some kind of dream, something he would wake up from. It was real. He wasn't coming home.

My first reaction was to pick up the phone and call someone — anyone — to share this awful realisation.

But who was there to call?

Continued overleaf.

Complete Story by SARAH BURKHILL

DAY OF RECKONING
Continued from previous page.

Six months ago, when Guy went away, people were marvellous. They rallied round, offering sympathy and support, and helping in any way they could.

But I didn't need help then, because I didn't believe it, not really. I was convinced it was all just a mistake, something that would sort itself out and everything would be fine again.

Now, when I have to accept that everything will not be fine again, people assume that I must have adjusted and learned to cope.

But how can a woman learn to cope with the fact that her husband loves another woman?

It happens to other people, friends, film stars and characters in magazines, but not to me. Not to Louise Barnes, 36 years old and married for almost 18 years, with a son called Adam and a one-eyed terrier called Nelson.

And yet it has.

Looking back, I'm amazed at how dense I was, how completely and utterly stupid. But then, perhaps I didn't want to recognise the signs that were before me.

There was nothing terribly obvious anyway; no lipstick on his collar or smell of scent, those things that are supposed to start a red alert for every wife.

Of course, there was extra time spent "at the office", but on top of that there were more subtle signs.

I should have spotted Guy's air of preoccupation, his changing moods, the odd way he started buying new clothes without being nagged into it. He became quite trendy, in fact.

And there was something else, something odder, perhaps even more significant. Rugged, unromantic Guy started listening to love songs, of all things — particularly those by one singer he had never paid much attention to before.

Time and again he would play the same disc, listening intently to the words as if they conjured up special, private pictures for him.

Oh, Mandy, you came and you gave without taking . . .

Why didn't I realise these things? Why was it only afterwards that it seemed they'd been blazoned across the sky in neon lights?

Afterwards . . . after that dreadful night when Guy came home, poured himself a whisky, and told me.

It was so abrupt, that's what I couldn't understand. I thought at first that I had misheard him, then that it was some kind of joke.

"Louise — I'm leaving home. I've met someone else. I want to live with her."

Those words repeated themselves so often in my mind during the next weeks, as if, night after night, I was compelled to relive the scene.

What a silly scene it was, too — like something from one of the soap operas on television, with all the same corny lines we hear again and again. It had never occurred to me before that writers use such scenes

150

because they're true, because that's how it actually is.

"I'm sorry, love, I didn't mean it to be this way. It just — just happened."

"But why? Why are you doing this? What's gone wrong?"

"I don't know. I don't understand it properly myself. I wish I did."

Guy had shrugged, as if by that action he could brush all complications away.

"We met at work. She's in the advertising department and we — got to know each other, had lunch a few times. And then —" He had shaken his head and turned his hands up in a gesture which said, Just one of these things.

"Don't worry about money or the house or anything," he had assured me. "I'll make sure you and Adam —"

"Tell me about her," I had interrupted rather harshly.

"Not much to tell. She's twenty-two, dark-haired and her name's Mandy."

Mandy? How I laughed when he said that. I thought of my 40-year-old husband mooning about like a teenager, and I laughed and laughed until the laughter turned to hysteria and I sank into a chair and shook uncontrollably.

Guy had looked uncomfortable then, uneasy, as if he'd have liked to turn and run, escape this anguished woman who was making things so uncivilised.

Perhaps that's why I had managed to pull myself together and gather what resources I had left and speak calmly.

"What are you going to do, then?" I had asked him.

"I — we've — applied for a transfer to the London office. I've got an agency to rent us a flat there. We start a week on Monday."

All that planning! All the arrangements made, and yet not a word to me! That seemed the greatest betrayal of all.

"And until then?"

"I'll wait until Adam gets in, and try to explain to him," he'd said. "Then — well, best that I go right away, I think, don't you?"

Of course I hadn't thought that. I thought it best that he stay, and listen to me, let me make him understand what a mistake it all was. Best that he forget this girl and remain where he belonged, with his wife and son.

But I didn't say that. I just sat and watched quietly while he packed a few clothes. I wondered why my brain didn't seem to function correctly, and why I couldn't think of anything to say. Why didn't I yell and scream and throw things? In the back of my mind the word "civilised" taunted me.

I thought of plenty in the next weeks, of course, acting out different, contrary scenes in my head.

There was the one where Guy walked in, contrite and humbled, and begged me to forgive him and take him back. Magnanimously I would hold out my arms and he would come to me, tell me what a fool he had been.

DAY OF RECKONING

And then the reverse of that — the one in which I looked at him coldly and told him to go back to his precious Mandy, that he was no longer necessary in my life.

How I loved him, how I hated him! At one in the morning it would be all my fault, I had driven him away. And then, as the clock chimed twice, he would be an ungrateful wretch who thought of no-one but himself.

Gradually, though, these conflicting emotions settled and I resigned myself to waiting. I decided that was the way. Time would fix everything and I would just sit and wait until Guy got over this fling, until life got back to . . . not to normal . . . it would never be that — but to some shadow of what it had been before.

With that decision made, things seemed easier. I got a job — just part-time work doing accounts at the local garage, which kept me occupied during the day.

But in the evenings I had time to think, to agonise over where I had failed, to wonder about the strange woman who had borrowed my husband.

Mandy. Try as I would, I couldn't visualise her properly, and she became a beautiful, out-of-focus face flickering behind my eyes.

One day, leafing through a magazine, I saw a photograph of a stunning, dark-haired model called Mandy, and her face became the one fixed in my mind as that of Guy's Mandy.

It was quite a disappointment to find she wasn't like that at all. Wendy Patterson, a friend whose husband works for the same firm, showed me a copy of the staff magazine. From a picture on page four, taken at the London office annual dance, Guy and his girl looked out at me.

She was quite ordinary looking: small and dark, nicely dressed with a pretty smile. But ordinary. I wondered what hidden magic she possessed that had lured Guy away from me, and from his son.

Thinking of Adam, I am reminded of the time, and I go through to the kitchen, to see to the evening meal.

Solid, unshakeable Adam, the stoic! What a help he has been to me. Sometimes I wonder if he misses his father more than he says, or if the occasional visit and the phone calls are really enough for him.

They were never as close as I would have liked them to be, so perhaps Adam's acceptance isn't entirely a facade. Oh, they got on well enough. There were no fights or disagreements or bad feeling.

But . . . maybe it was because they were so different that they had to work so hard at finding a real interest in each other.

Guy is the sporty type, who enjoys doing things, being active. He likes slapstick humour, and football, and being one of a crowd.

Adam is a more private person, studious, more thoughtful, different.

I hear his key in the lock now, and his big bag of books being dumped in the hallway.

"What's for tea? Ah, good. Chicken." He pinches a wedge of tomato from the plate and I chase him off.

"Can we eat early tonight? I'm going round to Bobby's. He's doing an end-of-term finance report for the swimming club, and I said I'd help."

He bends down to pat Nelson, who has come indoors in search of sustenance, and I put the potatoes on to boil.

Later, as we sit opposite each other at the breakfast bar, Adam looks thoughtful. "We saw the careers master today," he says. "Old Bertram. He had us in one at a time and gave us a pep talk on next session being our final year at school and 'the time for decision' and all that."

"Oh? That shouldn't present much of a problem for you. I thought you were set on accountancy."

That's what he's had in mind for years now. He has always been fascinated by figures.

"Yes, I know." He toys with a piece of potato. "But I suppose I hadn't really thought about anything else. Mr Bertram was talking about all sorts of careers that might be good for me. He's given me some literature."

Adam abandons the chicken salad and fetches his bag from the hall. He comes in smiling.

"Look," he says, turning pamphlets out on to the table. "There's so much to choose from, so many things I could do."

Suddenly he looks shy. "It's exciting in a way, isn't it? Starting out, with decisions to make and everything in front of you?

"Oh, I know things aren't easy at the moment, jobwise. But you can still make it, if you've got guts and determination, and you're . . ."

He tails off, now blushing, as if half-ashamed at letting me see the hopes and enthusiasm inside his head. "Oh, well — you know what I mean."

I smile across at him. "Yes, Adam. I know what you mean."

He has been gone for half an hour when I realise I didn't tell him about Guy's letter, and the little half-brother or half-sister that he is to have.

But he has so much on his mind at the moment, so many other things to think about.

My dear, darling Adam. How proud I am of him. How happy I am that he has his whole life ahead, uncharted territory for him to explore — unlike me.

Yet, perhaps in one sense it is the same for me. Growing up will force

SILENCE REIGNS

Love and laughter
fill the air
In a home
with children there.
When they grow
and leave the fold,
It seems to be
so bare and cold.

Happy were
their childhood days,
Even with
their impish ways.
No time to spare
or stop and think,
Under my feet
at the kitchen sink.

Life was full
we lived each day,
Tried our best
to show the way.
But time moves on
so must we,
Being thankful
for our family.

— Mrs B. E.,
Tyne & Wear.

DAY OF RECKONING

changes in Adam's life — and he welcomes them. Getting divorced will force changes in mine — and I am afraid of them.

Why? I wonder. Why am I so afraid, when my son is so hopeful? Because I am older, perhaps? Too old for change? Yet some people don't think 36 is old.

Perhaps there is another reason, too. For the first time in my life, I am alone, depending solely on myself. I had my parents to care for me, to make all the decisions. And then there was Guy, taking over where they left off.

Now there is me — only me. It's an interesting thought and I look in the mirror to see this person who has sole responsibility for Louise Barnes.

She has mousey hair, the kind that would look more attractive with a blonde rinse. She has blue eyes and a wide mouth, quite a pretty face in a "capable" sort of way.

And there is something else about her, something I have just noticed. She looks alive.

For the first time in years, she is faced with a challenge.

That's frightening, of course. But there is more than fear in those reflected eyes. There is hope, too. And a strange new kind of . . . excitement?

I square my shoulders. Tomorrow I'm going to meet that challenge. I'll go out and look for another job, a proper job. And if I can't find one — well, then I'll re-train. There are plenty of courses available.

Years ago there was a brain lurking somewhere in that head. It can't have disappeared, can it? I feel a sense of excitement.

I've decided — I'll stop waiting for Guy to come back and fix that chipped shelf in the corner. I'll do it myself. Now.

I hunt in the kitchen cupboard for sandpaper to smooth it over, then stop. No, I won't do that. If I re-do one little bit, the rest of the paintwork will look faded, and that would never do. Instead, I'll re-paint the whole room. I'll go out tomorrow and buy white paint, and I'll do it!

It won't be as good a job as Guy would have made, probably. But it will be my job, my very own achievement!

I walk round the rest of the house, peering into corners and examining surfaces.

The wallpaper in the kitchen is past its best. And the bedroom . . . I've never really liked the bedroom in that stark blue colour. Pink would be nice, or pale lilac maybe.

I'll think about it. I can have it any way I want. Tartan, if I fancied it. Or red and green stripes with purple curtains! The choice is mine.

Suddenly there is so much to do, so many things needing attention.

But I'll cope. A day at a time, one step at a time, I'll do it. There will be set-backs, I know, new things to learn, new problems to deal with. And loneliness, too, for a time . . .

But I'll do it.

And what's more, I'm beginning to look forward to it already. □

Complete Story by ELIZABETH ASHCROFT

She was afraid to face him — this man from her past.
Would he remember her and their . . .

Time Of Enchantment

I NEVER thought there'd be so many people here in the bookshop. In front of me a bowler-hatted business man is trying to look unconcerned. Perhaps he, too, is waiting to get the autograph from the visiting celebrity — for a travel-mad thirteen year old daughter — like me?

Continued overleaf.

TIME OF ENCHANTMENT
Continued from previous page.

A woman behind me in the queue is sucking peppermints and making a fuss of a white poodle in her arms. The dog struggles, yipping, and one of its paws rakes across my new suede winter coat. I sigh and accept her apologies. All the while my mind is on the man seated behind the desk, bent earnestly over a pile of books, autographing them. I can only see the back of his head. But it was just the same, the dark, untidy hair straggling on his neck, still worn too long. Unaccountably my heart begins to bump loudly. Suddenly I know I can't face him.

I turn abruptly, cannoning into the poodle. It gives a shrill yelp. I'm hemmed in on one side by a display case of best sellers and on the other by a stand of paperbacks, which sways alarmingly as I back into it.

I can't get out. Up ahead people are milling, heads craning, and I can even see Bill, the local photographer, who covers everything from baby shows to the local Donkey Derby. I can't leave now without making even more of a disturbance.

The queue shuffles on. The woman with the poodle drops her peppermints. I help her pick them up, scrabbling among people's feet, on the dusty floor.

"Have one?" she offers, and I take it, absently stuffing it into my pocket.

"Exciting, isn't it?" she twitters. "Not often we have a celebrity in our little town."

I shake my head. And suddenly I wish I'd never seen that paragraph tucked away in the local paper. I'd been unable to resist an exclamation, and Lisa came across, leaning companionably over the back of the chair.

Alan Adamson, travel writer, novelist, is coming to our local bookstore. He is autographing his new book, "Reminiscences Of A Roamer", on Thursday. Mr Adamson lived here for some time a few years ago and will be pleased to meet old friends.

Lisa, all puppy fat and huge brown eyes behind her glasses, leaned over me, smelling of my perfume she'd borrowed again.

"Alan Adamson! Oh, Mum! Can I go and see him? And get his autograph? Please!" Always curled up with a book, crazy to travel, Alan Adamson was her hero.

Howard, sprawled on the sofa, looked up sharply. He didn't say anything, but I sensed he was listening intently.

"School," I said succinctly to Lisa. "You can't skip school just for a glimpse of someone. Besides, to get his autograph you'd have to buy his book."

"It's my birthday next month," she said speculatively, with her eyes gleaming in a way I recognised.

"And you always ask me what I want."

"And you always say you'd prefer a surprise," I said sharply.

"This time I'd like his book, and his autograph. After all, if he's actually touched it —" Her voice tailed away and into the tiny waiting silence Howie spoke.

156

"Your mother knew him, Lisa. I'm sure she'd get his autograph for you."

Astonished, I stared at him. For years, Howard had never spoken of Alan Adamson.

He went on drily. "I'll buy you the book for your birthday. But I can't get his autograph. Your mother will have to do that."

How could he? What was he trying to do? But I knew I had to go, to face Alan again . . .

The queue shuffles forward slowly, and now there are only two in front of me. I hug the large shining book to my chest, feel the hard edge cutting into me. Nervously I riffle through the pages.

He probably won't even recognise me after all these years. He'll just scribble his name, and say, "Next please," in his low voice, and then it will all be over.

A word leaps out at me from the page. Enchantment. I read on slowly. *Into all our lives must come a period of tranquillity, which we look back upon with a sweet regret as a time of enchantment.*

And suddenly I am transported to a time when Lisa was five and Howie and I were going through the difficult patch most marriages seem to touch at some time. He'd been having trouble with his business, a builder's and do-it-yourself store, and seemed to have no time for me, Lisa, or our home. And money was short . . .

MY mother looked after Lisa and I signed on as a temp. Nervously I stared at the corrugated iron waves of the woman behind the desk in the agency.

"But — I wanted an office job — where I could meet people —"

She frowned. "I'm sorry. But your qualifications —" limited, I knew "— and no recent experience. I can't offer you anything at the moment."

There was a commotion outside then and a harassed receptionist appeared, trying vainly to stop a tall man with a very tanned face. He looked, I thought enviously, as though he'd just come back from the Mediterranean.

"Betty." His voice was deep, authoritative. "The last girl you sent me couldn't spell, didn't know the difference between a noun and a verb, and her coffee was atrocious." He hesitated, stared from Betty to me, and back again.

"Can you type?" he demanded fiercely.

I nodded.

"Got transport?"

"A — a bike," I stammered.

He turned to Betty Masters.

"When can she start?"

Helplessly she turned to me, and I recovered a little dignity.

"I can start on Monday. But I'd like first to know the salary, and hours. And," I added pointedly, "for whom I would be working."

Mrs Masters looked astonished. "But this is Alan Adamson, Mrs Grey. The writer."

TIME OF ENCHANTMENT

He'd just made news by selling the film rights to his latest novel, and had also been divorced, noisily. But he was younger than I'd expected. I flushed as he strode round the desk and named a salary I couldn't possibly refuse.

"Betty will tell you where I live. Wear trousers," he added unexpectedly, and banged out of the office, leaving me exhilarated and breathless.

On Monday I rode my ancient bike up the muddy lanes to Myrtle Cottage, huddled in the corner of a field. And I wore trousers, as ordered. Alan Adamson, I gathered, had rented the cottage for six months, and had already worked his way through three temps.

I rang the bell at the front and knocked at the back door. There was no reply. So I walked round the house and came to a halt, staring through an open window.

There was an old leaning conservatory outside what was presumably the living-room. Inside sat a hunched figure pecking away at a typewriter. He wore a thick, polo-necked sweater and horn-rimmed glasses, and he was shouting.

"Don't hover, girl! Tell me what you want then leave me in peace. Selling something, are you?"

By now I was wet, and cross myself. Did he expect me to work in that damp conservatory? No wonder all the other temps had fled.

"I am not selling anything, and I do have a name. I," I announced belligerently, "am Caroline Grey, and I am your new secretary."

Unexpectedly, he smiled.

"Caroline. Nice. Now, can you make coffee? And I want you to type this out with three copies. I'm behind schedule."

I was still annoyed. "Which do you want first? Coffee or typing?"

He looked astonished. Not many people stood up to him, I realised.

"Coffee." He looked at my mohair sweater and damp trousers. "Glad you dressed sensibly. It's cold out here."

So he did expect me to work out here. The rain drummed on the glass roof and ran dismally down the window panes. In one corner drooped a forlorn ivy plant, and a few elderly cane chairs leaned against each other for comfort.

"This is your office?"

"I work better out here. There's more room, and it's lighter and airier."

The wind rustled through a broken pane of glass and I shivered. Pneumonia beckoned.

"This was my grandparents' home," he said unexpectedly over coffee. He added, strangely, "Here, I feel safe."

I thought of his perilous adventures to get his photographs, the background to his novels, the stark photographs. "I see."

"No, you don't." He stared out at the dismal jungly garden, grey in the rain. "Here, I'm a boy again. Safe and cocooned from everything. Here, everything is waiting, fresh and new again."

I didn't understand, just stared at him. He shrugged impatiently.

TIME OF ENCHANTMENT

"You ever heard of writer's block? Well, I've got it. This is where I wrote my first book. Then, the garden was full of flowers, and this old conservatory was filled with plants. African violets, geraniums, trailing ivy everywhere. It was an enchanting place to me, then."

Suddenly he thumped his hand on the typewriter, and the keys jumped, jamming them together. "My brain's stopped functioning. Better make some more coffee," he added brusquely, as if regretting his outburst.

THAT was all I seemed to do those first few days, make coffee. He'd write something, I'd type it, then he'd throw it away, scowling. He was bad-tempered, untidy, and impossible to work for. I'd give it a week, I vowed miserably, sneezing. I didn't like the famous author, or his conservatory, or his coffee.

But I couldn't stand the bleakness. One morning I sneaked in a potted plant from my own kitchen and put it on a shelf by my chair.

It cheered the place up. So I brought another and another. But still he never mentioned it. I brought a cushion for my chair and one for his, and suddenly the conservatory began to look lived in.

Then one morning I found him bent over the typewriter, typing furiously. He frowned at me.

"Can I do anything?" I asked.

He shook his head, not even looking at me. "Coffee," he barked. I stamped to the dingy kitchen and made yet more coffee. I'd give in my notice right now, I fumed. Dogsbody, that's me. I'd tell him right now that I was leaving.

He was still typing when I took his coffee to him.

"Mr Adamson," I began shakily. "I have to tell you —"

He glowered at me, actually looking at me for the first time. "Be quiet!"

"Well what do you expect me to do?" I burst out angrily. "I can't just sit around making coffee all day, waiting for words of wisdom from your pen."

Now I'd get the sack, I thought. He wouldn't wait for me to give in my notice.

But to my astonishment he laughed.

"I'm afraid you'll have to, Carrie. Once I get going you'll be complaining of overwork. Now, disappear, there's a good girl."

He was turning on the charm, I thought crossly, and opened my mouth to tell him I was leaving. Then he spoke.

"You make the best coffee I've ever tasted."

Unaccountably, I flushed with pleasure. And I didn't give in my notice.

The next day he began working in earnest. I had to type frantically, almost non-stop. It had stopped raining. A pale watery sun came out and a faint warmth filled the conservatory. Alan, knowing the work was going well, began to unbend, to become human.

TIME OF ENCHANTMENT

"It looks like old times," he said, looking round the conservatory. "You brought it to life with your plants, Carrie."

I didn't think he'd noticed, and a glow touched me. "You could have done it yourself," I replied coolly.

He grinned. "I'll buy some next time I'm in town."

He did, too. Huge trailing ivy plants, which curled round our heads, and nodding pansies in little pots, and a spiky cactus.

Suddenly I began to feel at home there. I'd look at Howie, going off to work with a worried frown, or watch Lisa as she skipped off with my mother to go shopping, and wonder what was happening to me.

At odd moments, when I'd caught up with the work, I got out a hoe and weeded the borders of the overgrown garden. The daffodils appeared, nodding blithely at me in the sunshine. A few crimson tulips had sprouted under the apple trees, and without my realising it fully, spring had arrived. My face grew tanned, and my mother told me how well I looked, and I felt horribly guilty.

One morning Alan came to stand beside me as I weeded around some overgrown rose bushes.

"There used to be hyacinths here," he said with a trace of wistfulness.

I'd forgotten it had been his grandparents' home.

To my surprise he went into the old shed and reappeared with rusty secateurs.

"I'll prune the roses. I need some fresh air."

"But what about the book —"

He grinned. "Don't be a slave-driver. I have to have a rest sometime."

That began the pattern of our days. The sun shone, and the apple blossom was pink against the pale blue sky, and the conservatory was a riot of colour.

We worked hard, then pottered in the garden while he thought out the next chapter, or just talked to me about the plot, working it out in his mind. Therapy, he called it. Recharging his brain.

For me it was a time of sheer joy; almost as though I'd shed the cares of my marriage, my child, my home.

Oddly, Howie had never spoken of Alan, except when Lisa mentioned him once as I tucked her up in bed.

"What's your writer like, Mummy?" she'd asked sleepily, staring at me with those enormous brown eyes. "Is he old, with a beard?"

"She must have seen a picture of George Bernard Shaw," I said laughingly to Howie.

"Is he old?" he'd asked.

I hesitated, stroking Lisa's soft cheek and speaking to her.

"He's not got a beard, darling. And he's older than Daddy. And going a little grey," I added, remembering the scattering of grey in Alan's hair and forbearing to add that he was only a few years older than her father.

I noticed Howie staring at me across the low bed, then he turned away.

Once, Alan unexpectedly touched my cheek, almost as I'd touched Lisa's.

160

"If it hadn't been for you, Carrie, I'd never even have got started on my book," he said softly. "The place is almost exactly the way my grandparents had it. Peaceful."

My hands trembled and my heart began to beat faster. Oh, no, I thought. You're married to Howard. I thought of his silences, the way he studiously never mentioned my work, and I wondered if he had guessed. Guessed what? I told myself I just enjoyed my work, the salary. It was nothing to do with Alan·Adamson. But it was, and I knew it somewhere deep inside me.

Then one afternoon he got up swiftly from his desk. It was hot, a foretaste of summer, and the conservatory was stifling.

"I've had enough," he said. "And I'm sure you have too. Let's play truant."

"Truant?" I stared at him open-mouthed.

"Get out the deck chairs and sit in the sun. Have some lemonade under the apple tree the way I used to when I was a boy." He looked across at me as I dithered. "Carrie, if it hadn't been for you I would never have written this book. You've made the old place an enchantment again. A magical place. You're a bit of an enchantress yourself," he added, smiling.

I knew I was blushing. I got up hastily, and went for lemonade. How odd that he should put my own feelings about the cottage into words.

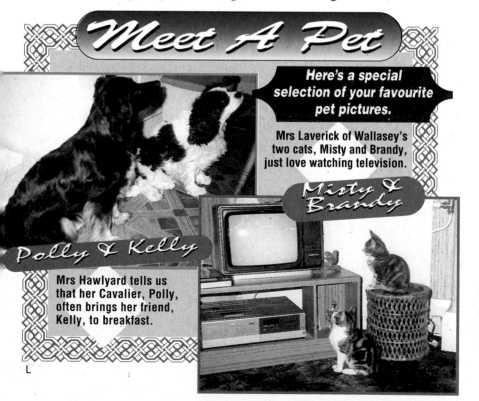

Meet A Pet

Here's a special selection of your favourite pet pictures.

Mrs Laverick of Wallasey's two cats, Misty and Brandy, just love watching television.

Misty & Brandy

Polly & Kelly

Mrs Hawlyard tells us that her Cavalier, Polly, often brings her friend, Kelly, to breakfast.

TIME OF ENCHANTMENT

We sat under the apple tree and he told me the book was nearly finished. I was filled with sadness.

Somehow, we sat there long after I should have started for home, watching the bees floating lazily across the flower border. I knew it was nearly over before it had even begun. Then out of the blue he spoke.

"I shall be leaving soon, Carrie."

I felt the glass in my hand begin to shake, and put it down hastily so that he wouldn't notice.

"Soon?" I said with forced calmness. To my astonishment he took my hand and held it firmly in his.

"To Israel. To research for a new book." He hesitated. "Carrie. You wouldn't come with me?"

I gasped. As his secretary, or something else? Something else — I knew it from his eyes.

The shock went right through me. I thought of Howie, his silence lately, of the years we'd been married, the way we leaned on each other. And Lisa, growing up. It would be the end of everything familiar.

And Alan — he'd been married and divorced, engaged two or three times. He was footloose, a wanderer. This, I told myself shakily, was just another little romance to him. A way to pass the summer.

"I can't," I said. "You know I can't."

"No?" he stared reflectively at the cottage, serene in the evening sunlight. "I didn't think you would, Carrie.

"I shall miss it here," he added after a silence.

So shall I, I thought. But I shall miss you more. And what will happen to the conservatory? It will lie empty again, neglected, and the garden will soon grow wild again. My enchanted garden, I thought, blinking back stupid tears.

His hand was firm on mine. "Carrie, it's been a time of sheer enchantment, working here with you. You brought the old cottage back to life again, gave me confidence again. For that I will always be grateful."

And you've broken my heart, I mourned foolishly. But it was wise, I knew, not to prolong this. I stood up swiftly, and tripped over the small table. I stumbled, then I was in his arms, and he was kissing me for the first and last time.

As I left the cottage, shaken and unsure, a few minutes later, I saw a familiar car disappear round the corner. Our car.

I wondered, with terror-stricken guilt, if Howie had come to meet me, wondering why I was so late. Had he seen me with Alan in the garden? He seemed even more silent than usual that evening, and I felt sure he suspected something.

After a sleepless, guilt-ridden night, I knew I would never go back to Myrtle Cottage. And it was very early that morning when Lisa took ill with appendicitis and was whisked off to hospital. I had no time for work. Alan and Myrtle Cottage were pushed right out of my mind.

By the weekend Lisa was out of danger. I remembered Alan and phoned to explain, but there was no reply. I held the phone and listened to the distant, ringing bell and knew with sadness that the enchanted time was over.

Howie came into the hall and saw me standing there. He took the phone from my hand, raising his eyebrows questioningly. He'd been so strong, these past few days, I didn't know how I would have coped without him.

Suddenly I wondered how on earth I could even have contemplated leaving him, and Lisa, for a will-o'-the-wisp like Alan Adamson. I knew that he'd left without even saying goodbye.

I stood in the familiar hall and smiled shakily at Howie.

"Wrong number," I said, and went to make tea.

Now, I have reached the desk, and Alan takes the book from my hand without raising his eyes. He looks tired, there are more lines under his eyes. He looks, somehow, dissatisfied. I wonder fleetingly what it would have been like, then I start, as he speaks. "Name?"

Without thinking, I answer. "Carrie."

He looks up. He doesn't recognise me, I think with horror. Have I grown so old, in eight years?

"Sorry. Lisa," I amend hastily, and his eyes meet mine and recognition touches them. He smiles, the smile I dreamed of for months after he left.

"Any special message?"

Now I begin to think, oddly relieved, that he doesn't remember. I'm just one of dozens of familiar faces he's seen on this visit.

"Just to Lisa. My daughter," I add, and he scribbles across the page, frowning a little. I watch him, and know that it would never have worked. I am safe here in my familiar little town with my family

I take the book, and he smiles at me. I look at him for the last time. He is nearly grey now over the temples. Harassed-looking, already picking up the next book. And as he takes it he murmurs something.

"I'm glad you came."

I stare. He has recognised me, then, and an odd gladness fills me. The woman behind shuffles her feet impatiently.

"Thank you, Alan," I say, and he nods, understanding, scribbles again. I leave the queue, and Alan, and walk slowly to the shop entrance. And there, in our car parked near the door, is a familiar face.

It's Howie. My dear, dependable Howie wearing a worried frown. Come to make sure I don't run off with the visiting celebrity. All those years, and he's never once mentioned his fear. Laughter bubbles in me. I flick the book open and read the inscription. My step suddenly falters. He did remember. All of it.

To Lisa, I read. May she have a time of enchantment some day too.
Alan Adamson.

I turn. Our eyes meet, and he waves. I wave back, blinking a little.
Then I go out to join Howie. ☐

163

Complete
Story by
ROSEMARY
ALEXANDER

An Everyday Miracle

S OMETIMES the fear would descend quite suddenly, like a black cloud obliterating the sunlight. Then Anna could no longer take a delight in their new home, the flint-walled farmhouse overlooking the downs and the distant sea.

Sometimes the fear stalked her as she walked down the lane with Jenny to collect the children from school, or chatted to Mrs Heaseman about the latest village scandal.

Sometimes, when she woke in the morning, Anna dared not open her eyes to confront it, though Ricky was there, warm and substantial, a match for the most menacing phantom.

But she couldn't confide in him . . . could not say simply: "Ricky, I'm absolutely terrified by the thought of having children."

It would be such a ridiculous admission from a bright, independent girl, so apparently well-adjusted to the modern world.

If she had been able to talk to someone who appreciated the problem — to her mother, for instance — things might not have been so bad. Her mother lived 200 miles away, though, and had troubles of her own.

A few weeks ago Anna's father had been rushed into hospital, and although he was on the mend now, his wife had enough to bear without the added burden of a neurotic daughter. Anna kept her letters to her mother bright and cheerful, betraying no hint of her ever-present fear.

Darling Mum,

I honestly think we're just about straight at last! The house is lovely, and the curtains you sent fit the spare-room window perfectly. I can't wait for your visit at Easter. Tell Dad, if he isn't strong enough to travel by then, I'll howl so loudly you'll hear me even in the North!

Ricky loves his new job. The other vets in the practice are very easy to get along with. Of course, he's out a lot. This is an area of horsy folk, so he's for ever immersed in warbles and bots and broken knees!

It can be lonely here, but I've already made one really good friend, Jenny Miller. She and Miles have a cottage 200 yards from here, and three gorgeous children; two at the village school, and a toddler who's into everything.

Continued overleaf.

165

Jenny's a very talented artist and she works in an old barn they've turned into a studio. She's painting my portrait, in a highly-complimentary fashion, though Ricky doesn't like it. He claims she's making me look like a scared, wild pony . . .

And he was right, too. With uncanny perception, Jenny had caught the fear behind her cool, dark-haired prettiness.

"You're not a bit like that!" Ricky had protested. "Jenny, you're depicting my wife as a fey, haunted creature, not the trendy town bird I fell in love with."

Oh, but it is me, Ricky, she longed to confess, not daring to disenchant him. His love for her might diminish, once he glimpsed the coward sheltering behind a mask of sophistication.

TIME and again, Anna was on the point of admitting her secret to Jenny, but shame held her back . . . Shame of her own flawed personality.

One day they stood waiting together in the tiny post office-cum-general store, while Jenny's children brooded, soberly and long, over the weighty matter of which sweets to spend their pocket money on.

"Wait until you get a few of these around you, Mrs Bannister!" Mrs Heaseman, the assistant, joked.

Though kindly meant, Anna felt the old fear overwhelming her. She managed to force a smile and a light answer.

"I'm afraid I'm not the motherly type, Mrs Heaseman. I'll probably start looking for a job, now we've settled down."

"You'll never do that, Mrs Bannister!" The round, rosy face registered mild disapproval. "A vet needs a wife to take his phone calls, and deal with emergencies. You'll have enough on your plate with that!"

"Oh, we've got a central clinic to deal with appointments and emergencies, Mrs Heaseman. Ours is a very modern practice, not the old-fashioned kind of set-up."

Anna smiled again . . . kept on smiling, so that neither of them would suspect how the remark had churned up her emotions.

"Well, you'll not get folk round here abandoning the old ways," Mrs Heaseman replied disapprovingly.

"Are you all right, Anna?" Jenny asked, as they strolled back through the village. Instinctively Anna knew her subterfuge hadn't worked. Jenny was far too sensitive to be deceived.

"Oh, perfectly. It's just that Mrs Heaseman gets under my skin occasionally. She's such an old busybody."

"She doesn't mean to be. Gossip is our way of showing we're interested in our neighbours. You mustn't mind, Anna. Country folk tend to be on the nosy side."

"And I'm town bred!" Anna felt a pang of homesickness. For a moment, she longed for the quiet, orderly routine she had known before marriage. Then there had just been the three of them: Mum, Dad and

Anna, the centre of their existence. She had known exactly where she was going and life held no terrors. She was sheltered and secure.

"I suppose, in time, you and Ricky will have a family?" Jenny continued. "He'll be a marvellous father."

It was the opening Anna had waited for, and she grasped it eagerly.

"I think we'll probably . . ." She was unable to continue because Emma, who had been racing ahead, fell and grazed her leg. In the subsequent uproar, the chance for intimate conversation vanished.

There'll be other opportunities, Anna consoled herself — though somehow she felt doomed to endure her fear alone.

Ricky was not unsympathetic. When she'd reversed the car into Mrs Heaseman's ice-cream sign and on another occasion burned a joint of beef to a cinder, he had merely laughed, and said:

"I don't expect miracles, darling. I fell in love with a smart, competent secretary. Perfect housewives aren't made in a couple of months!"

But the present dilemma was infinitely worse than a dented bumper or a ruined meal.

Anna decided to behave, therefore, as though she were in her element, learning to run a home, discussing his whereabouts with worried patients who couldn't be bothered to go through the correct procedure and contact the clinic. For hours on end this kept her mind occupied until literally out of the blue the phantom launched another attack.

THE day which provoked the crisis followed the now-familiar pattern. She spent the morning cleaning the sitting-room and washed blankets in the afternoon before going down to the village.

When she returned at about five, she found her husband had arrived home early.

He was in the kitchen attending to a bedraggled bundle of black and white fur he had placed on a thick wad of newspapers on the table. Ricky was angrier than she had ever seen him before.

"I found her dumped at the edge of the main road," he explained in answer to her query. "I'd like to get my hands on the callous brute who pushed her out of his car and left her to fend for herself."

"Is she badly hurt? She's trembling all over."

Anna patted the mongrel, and the shaggy tail thumped briefly.

"It's mostly shock. Apart from a few scratches, and a rather nasty gash on her shoulder, she's not seriously injured. But she's going to have pups in the very near future . . . which is probably why her owner decided to get rid of her."

The strength drained from Anna's limbs as panic engulfed her.

"You mean she's going to have puppies on our kitchen table!"

"Well, not at this precise moment! We'll have time to make her a comfortable bed. The trouble is, what she's just been through may hurry things on, and I've got to go out again. The Dacres' pony has severe colic. You'll have to keep an eye on her while I'm out."

Continued on page 170.

A Fruitful Feast

The birds and the beasts of the Strath throng to Croft Douglas for the annual banquet of berries, where there's more than enough to go round . . .

MULTI-COLOURED rows of jam and jelly lined along the shelves of our larder with almost military precision have to bear testimony to the fact that this has been a bumper year for berries.

It started with the strawberries, followed by the gooseberries, mostly growing wild, the bushes bowed down with their burden of fruit, all of which made for the beginnings of a big battle between those who sought to gather this harvest of goodness.

First, the poultry pick the berries from the lower branches until they can reach no higher. Then the wood pigeons come with a clatter of wings. Gooseberries are their favourite fruit and this is the only time these ever-so-shy birds venture close to Croft Douglas.

They seem to sense just when the berries are at their succulent best and, fluttering amongst the topmost branches, they eat their fill.

Breakfast begins for them with the first beam of the dawn's early light and, being an early riser, too, I am the first to disturb them.

But they only return as soon as I re-enter the house.

Nothing will induce Irralee to rise and pick a single berry until she has had a mug of steaming-hot tea and a substantial slice of well-marmaladed toast! So, while I am making the tea and toast, the wood pigeons move in to take advantage and tuck in.

Just a little later, there was another "todo" on the raspberry canes loaded with rosy red fruit, which resulted in a continuous sparring session with the speckled song thrushes. Then we had a contest with the yellow-billed blackbirds over a huge crop of blackcurrants that hung heavily from the bushes like bunches of black grapes.

It all had to end sometime, and it did, in a draw, with both birds and humans coming to the conclusion that each had had more than their fair share.

This was silently seconded by the little field and wood mice who had worked, day and night, collecting the fallen berries and storing away what they couldn't eat at the time.

That's how this year's soft fruits were sampled, savoured and stored for much-needed sustenance in the wintertime.

THE really warm spell started just before the middle of May and awakened the northern vipers from their hibernation. The adders, as they are commonly called, slither out of their hiding holes to sun themselves on some sheeptrack, freshly-turned molehill, or on the warm stones near the water's edge.

Adders carry venomous poison, but the

GIDEON'S WAY

More impressions of life from the Highlands of Scotland, by Gideon Scott May, observer of people and nature alike...

long, flashing tongue is only an organ of smell. The poison lies in the fangs in the front of the snake's upper jaw.

But adders, I am sure, are far more afraid of humans than humans are of them and, if you are fond of hillwalking, climbing in the Highlands, or rambling across the moorland heather, stride out and "boldly go", because the adders, if there are any about, are very sensitive to vibrations and will quickly disappear long before you are even near.

They say you are as likely to be struck by lightning as bitten by an adder, but it did happen to me.

It was my own fault entirely. I put my hand into a carefully-concealed partridge nest, just to see how many eggs there were, but there was something else coiled up cosily in the nest — a large adder.

To him, my hand must have been a bigger snake menacing him, so he struck, and I felt a sharp, burning bite before the adder slid over my arm, flicked out his tongue and disappeared.

My right hand had two small puncture holes in it between my thumb and forefinger. I had been told always to open an adder bite, and drew the sharp blade of my knife gently across from one puncture hole to the other.

Despite continuously sucking at the wound, when I staggered into the doctor's surgery, my hand was a knuckle-less mass and my right arm resembled a rugby football!

The doctor was coolly clinical. He basked in a reputation for bringing babies safely into the world and didn't seem to be worried about some stupid snake-bitten fellow passing out.

He did make some attempt at saving me with a huge hypodermic needle, after which I felt faint and slumped in the surgery chair, but I felt better after the good doctor gave me a glass of something he said was certain to complete his cure for snake bite, although I wondered why he had one himself!

A BIG heron flies over our house almost every morning. He is on his way to a favourite pool where he is prepared to stand and wait, until suppertime, if necessary, for some unwary fish or frog.

I was walking along the lochside with Ceilidh, my little spaniel, when I spotted the heron standing under the tattered skirt of an old willow tree, with his long legs almost submerged, when suddenly he struck like lightning at something near the water's edge.

It was an adder he must have mistaken for an eel. I watched as the heron tossed the snake high in the air. It finally landed with a thump on the sand at the edge of the water, while the heron took off, flapping his huge wings and croaking disconsolately.

Meantime, Ceilidh and I had a closer look at the adder. It wasn't moving and Ceilidh didn't want to go too near.

She has a deep distrust of adders, but I picked it up with my thumb and forefinger placed carefully behind its head. It was a young male with the "V" for a viper sign printed boldly on the back of its head.

I thought the heron had given the adder a fatal blow, but no, it was coming round rapidly.

Adders have no eyelids and their slit-like, vertical pupils open and shut like stage curtains. This one was surveying me in a friendly fashion, so I laid it down and let it go with the thought that, should our paths ever cross again, it wouldn't bite me.

After all, if you haven't got faith, then you haven't got anything. ∎

AN EVERYDAY MIRACLE

Continued from page 167.

"But you can't leave me alone with her, Ricky!" Anna protested weakly, her heart thumping wildly.

"Why ever not, darling? She's a tough little animal. And, after all, it's a natural process."

"But I've no idea what to do!"

"Just reassure her — let her know you're around. She'll do the rest for herself . . . and I won't be away long."

Attempting to quell her alarm, Anna found a stout cardboard box and lined it with a remnant of carpet. The unexpected guest, lapping warm milk from a pudding basin, viewed her activity with approval.

"There . . . does that suit you?" Gingerly, Anna placed the mongrel into its snug retreat. "I can't go on referring to you as 'dog'. I think I'll call you Daisy, because you were found on a grassy verge. Is that all right, pet?"

The shaggy tail thumped against the cardboard, and two brown eyes beamed a grateful thank you.

Somehow, the kitchen looked more complete, with Daisy's box in the space between the sink and the fridge. Her occasional sigh had a friendly note.

I'll ask Ricky to get her a proper basket tomorrow, Anna thought, as she set the table.

By eight o'clock, when Ricky still hadn't returned, Anna's imagination was working overtime. Then the phone rang.

"Bill Halland saw my car parked outside Dacres' place and rushed in to tell me his thoroughbred mare's started to foal. I don't anticipate problems, but he's in such a state, I agreed to stay to supper and keep an eye on her."

"What about the puppies . . .?"

"You know where to contact me if anything goes wrong . . . though it's highly unlikely. Just talk to her if she seems upset. It won't take long."

Her heart sinking, Anna replaced the receiver. He's got no consideration, she thought. I'm not a country girl — I don't know how to deal with these situations. Raging against him helped to subdue the rising panic.

When Anna went back to the kitchen, Daisy was awake. The whimpers had become insistent, acquiring a slightly different note. Anna crouched beside the box and stroked the mongrel's velvety ears.

"What is it, pet? I wish I could help you."

The brown eyes pleaded, as if saying, "Please don't leave me."

"Of course I won't leave you," Anna reassured her.

What was her own terror compared with this wordless plea of sympathy?

A SICKLE moon hung over the downs when the sound of Ricky's car moved gradually nearer up the hill. Anna ran out to greet him and, before he had switched off the engine, gasped:

"Daisy's had her puppies. Come and see them . . . two tiny replicas of their mum!"

Radiating maternal pride, Daisy thumped her tail, as Ricky approached and bent over her. Plainly, she expected congratulations.

"Not quite replicas! One's a dog. Aren't you a clever little mongrel?" Accepting the praise as her due, Daisy nuzzled her puppies back into the warmth of her fur. "And weren't you lucky to have your own personal midwife in attendance!"

He reached out to draw Anna into the charmed circle round the makeshift bed.

"Her personal midwife didn't do a thing. It was all over before I realised what had happened," Anna confessed.

And then, quite suddenly, the whole affair was too much for her and she was weeping uncontrollably.

"Hey, what's this all about?" Ricky stood up, and pulled out his handkerchief.

"Oh, Ricky, I'm glad you're back. I've been so frightened . . ."

"Because a little stray produced a family? Come off it, love, that's not the whole story."

"No, it isn't. I've been scared for ages . . . Well, for the past five weeks to be exact."

"Scared of what? This is the first I've heard of it."

"I'm going to have a baby at the beginning of October and I'm simply petrified. I've never had anything to do with babies and I don't know how I'll ever go through with it."

"You're expecting a baby . . .? That's marvellous news! Why didn't you tell me, love? I wondered why you were so quiet and edgy, and just put it down to homesickness and anxiety about your father's illness. It's not like you."

"I'm not like me! That's partly the trouble. And I couldn't bring myself to mention it because you're so used to confinements and that kind of thing. It seemed so silly to make a fuss. Then the longer I kept it to myself, the worse it became . . ."

Yet, as she spoke, a strange thing happened. The fear which had haunted her for the past six weeks curled up and died. Having this baby would be an experience which would deepen and strengthen their love. Why had she striven so perversely to avoid it?

"You were silly, darling. A sure way to aggravate horror is to keep it locked up to multiply in secret. Admittedly, I'm forever attending confinements — it's part of my job — but didn't it occur to you that this is different? This is our own baby, and absolutely unique."

"I realise that now, and I'm not frightened . . . at least, only as nervous as a girl normally is over her first baby! I can't imagine why I made such a thing of it. As you say, it's a perfectly natural process."

And Daisy drummed the side of the box with her tail, as though to confirm the statement. Anyone can be a little nervous, the brown eyes said clearly. But just look at the joy we mothers have in store!   □

COMPLETE
STORY BY
**LYNDA
FRENCH**

YOU'LL LIKE HIM . . . PHILOSOPHER . . . ELDER
STATESMAN . . . ERSTWHILE PHILANDERER —
WITH STILL A SURPRISE OR TWO IN STORE FOR
ALL OF US.

OLD HENRY'S VIEW OF THE WORLD

H ENRY looked up, startled out of his blissful daydreaming, as the convoy of cars whizzed past down the narrow lane that snaked its way across the bottom of the valley. He resented his peace being disturbed, and he gave them a dirty look from his vantage point on the hill.

Continued overleaf.

Why was life so urgent nowadays? Everybody ran here and there, as if they hadn't a minute to spare. Henry had far more interesting things to do than rush about, missing everything the world had to offer.

He shook his head, refusing to let the nasty things bother him, and as the earlier peace returned, Henry felt life was on the whole good, simple and kind. He relaxed once more as he felt the strong, late spring sun beating down and warming his old bones.

It was the time of the year for romance, and heady new feelings were growing, along with the new season's steady progress. Once again, Henry could feel the spring blood coursing through his veins, just like every year that had gone before, and the long, hard winter seemed nothing more than a bad dream.

Even now any flighty young female could turn his head, and Jilly had done just that, with all her sweet softness, and that strangely forward shyness of youth around her.

Yes, she had a very bad effect on him, did Jilly, sending his old heart pounding away in sheer excitement.

Was it because she seemed to bring back the distant days of his own lost youth?

Lost, because his memory wasn't quite what it used to be, and he couldn't always summon up that earlier Henry.

But, sometimes, if he concentrated hard enough, he could relive those faraway years to liven up those few odd days when he felt a little under the weather.

He looked back, now, over his long life, in the same way that he gazed across the valley to the distant hills, with a bittersweet longing for something he couldn't quite reach. Then he stopped trying to see the impossible, closed his eyes for a moment, and conjured up those very earliest days on the farm.

The freedom to enjoy himself, chasing and playing, showing off in front of his mother, the complicated simplicity of farm life, with its rich, earthy smells, and always in the background, the farmer working hard.

HENRY, too, had worked hard for most of his life, not on the farm, but at Bertram Budden's Brewery. At first he'd felt strange, lost, in the town, but soon he'd found a friendly niche at "Treble B's", as they were affectionately known.

He was proud to be part of the huge combine, now that they had revived the smartly-turned-out old drays, pulled by their spanking teams, the beer barrels stacked high at the back. The brewery had become a much photographed tourist attraction, with the drays in their gleaming buttercup yellow livery.

In a sudden fit of nostalgia, Henry wondered about his old friends, Jess and Mike, and . . . now, whatever happened to poor Daniel? He missed their cheerful companionship, and he hoped they were all enjoying a happy retirement like himself.